American Wood & Metal Planes

From the Collection of the
D'Elia Antique Tool Museum

Andrew D'Elia

American Wood & Metal Planes

From the Collection of the
D'Elia Antique Tool Museum

Published by the

D'Elia Antique Tool Museum

Post Office Box 164
Scotland, Connecticut 06264
www.deliatoolmuseum.com

Design & Production

Norman R. Forgit
Hanson, Massachusetts 02341

Printing

John P. Pow Company, Inc.
Boston, Massachusetts 02127

Further Reading

This book is intended as a guide to some of the most
interesting and important planes on exhibit at the
D'Elia Antique Tool Museum. Further reference materials
on these and other planes in the collection can be found
in the following books:

**Patented Transitional & Metallic Planes in America
(Volume I & Volume II)**
Roger K. Smith

A Guide to the Makers of American Wooden Planes
Emil & Martyl Pollak
4th Edition, Revised by Thomas L. Elliott

Table of Contents

Foreword

It is hard to believe that it was 40 years ago that I purchased my first wood plane. It was an E.B. Jackson, Newfane, Vermont, crown molder for the sum of $35.00. I had no idea that the plane was rare and was marked with the maker's name. Little did I realize then that this purchase at a small country auction in New Hampshire would be the beginning of a lifetime of collecting planes. I still have this plane, and it is proudly displayed at the D'Elia Antique Tool Museum.

While working in Leominster, Massachusetts, years ago, I bought and restored an 18th century house in New Ipswich, New Hampshire. My wife, Anna Mae, and I shared antiquarian interests. Roger Smith and Ken Roberts, who became two of the leading authorities on old tools lived in our general neighborhood, and we would see each

other at flea markets where we both shared our interests and competed for "finds". Through them I learned of and joined the Early American Industries Association, an organization of tool enthusiasts who came to the subject from many different viewpoints. At meetings of the EAIA I met others – Herman Freedman, William Hilton, John and Paul Kebabian, and Thomas Relihan – who shared their considerable knowledge and collecting experience with me, helping me to refine and focus my interest. Planes, and particularly patented planes, became my passion, resulting in a collection that now numbers about 1,400 examples.

In 1982 I founded my own company, Atlantic Packaging, in Norwich, Connecticut. We moved to Scotland, Connecticut, a colonial town in the eastern part of the

state, known as the birthplace of Samuel Huntington, a Revolutionary War Patriot, delegate to the Continental Congress, and signer of the Declaration of Independence. With a population of only about 1,700, it retains much of the flavor of a colonial farming community and has been a pleasant place for us to settle and continue the pursuit of our interests. There we bought and restored another 18th century house, not far from the center of town. After spending over 40 years of my life in the paperboard packaging field I made the decision to sell my company and retire. Once retired, I planned on doing a number of things I often thought about but never had time for while running a company on a daily basis. We wanted to travel, and I had a long-standing interest in woodworking.

A major decision confronting me was what to do with my extensive plane collection. I decided to investigate the possible options available to help me determine the best solution. The first and most obvious option was to sell the collection. It could easily be disposed of at auction. Though selling was the easiest and fastest method, I was not comfortable with this idea. I had invested a great deal of time, effort, and money in the collection. As an entity, it brought together a considerable number of objects that illustrated the development of a significant industry and provided a great deal of information, readily available to anyone interested in studying it. Accordingly, I considered donating my collection to an interested family member with the stipulation it was not to be sold but preserved for future generations. No family members were interested in the collection, so I eliminated that option.

I seriously considered donating my collection to a museum, but finding a museum that would be the right match for my collection was not easy. Over the years I visited a number of museums and was given the privilege of visiting some of their storage areas. These areas contained objects donated as individual items or large collections. Many items had been in storage for years. My personal feeling was that most of the museum collections I saw would never be displayed, since sufficient display space is a problem for many museums. The thought of my collection ending up in some museum storage area and not displayed concerned me. For many perfectly understandable reasons, few museums are willing to accept donations to which permanent conditions are attached. Eventually it became apparent that in order to receive the assurances I wanted for my collection, I would have to establish my own museum.

The Town of Scotland had a library located in a small area of the town office building, formerly a schoolhouse. The library had outgrown this space and was searching for a new location to better serve the community. One proposal under consideration was to convert an old firehouse to a library. I had a number of discussions with Anna Mae about this, and we felt that the idea was a poor one. We wanted to help the town solve the library problem and decided to make a suggestion of our own. We proposed that the D'Elia Foundation would provide all the necessary funding for a new structure for a library/museum. The library would be under the control of the town and the D'Elia Foundation would run the museum to house and display my plane collection.

The town gratefully accepted our proposal. For the library and museum's site, we agreed upon a parcel of town-owned land on Brook Road, which had adequate buildable space for the structure. It was adjacent to the new firehouse, diagonally across from the elementary school, and was partially surrounded by wetlands that would be an ideal place for nature trails.

When the appropriate formalities had been completed, proposals for the project were published, and Schoenhardt Architects, Inc. of Simsbury was engaged to design a 7,000 square foot building of which 6,000 were to be the library, and a 1,000 square foot wing would be the museum.

The library was dedicated in 2005 and the museum the following year. We supervised the interior finish of the museum room with the selection and arrangement of the display cases. A particularly pleasing touch was the commission of a series of stained glass windows depicting some of the monuments in the history of planes, designed and crafted by Architectural Stained Glass of Brooklyn, Connecticut.

The museum initially opened displaying about 1,000 planes and today there are over 1,400. The museum is proud of its extensive collection of American patented planes, probably the largest collection on display at one location. Many are rare, and a number are the only known examples in existence. The large collection of American 18th century planemakers includes many rare makers such as Francis and John Nicholson, Cesar Chelor, O. Spicer, I. Jones, A. Hide, Doggett, Wetherel, and Ballou. Other displays feature the products of Stanley and Sargent, bench planes, carriage maker's, cooper's and other collectible planes. A featured collection comprises examples of the work of over one hundred Connecticut plane makers.

From time to time as the opportunities arise, we continue to acquire historically important planes and add them to the museum's collections. Since the museum's opening in 2006, it has received many compliments on the library/museum building as well as the museum's well-organized and pleasing displays. Articles in newspapers, trade magazines, and journals as well as enthusiastic comments from visitors have provided much favorable publicity for the museum.

We have produced this book to promote the D'Elia Antique Tool Museum and provide a keepsake for those who visit. It includes illustrations with captions of some 400 planes, including many unique examples, selected to provide a broad sampling of the 1,400 planes in the museum's collections. We hope the book will generate additional interest and support for The D'Elia Antique Tool Museum in Scotland, Connecticut.

Andrew D'Elia

Wood & Metal
Patent Planes

Knowles Jointer Plane

Inventor: Hazzard Knowles

Origin: Unknown

Patent Number & Date: None known.

Knowles type iron jointer with wood infill, 22 3/16" lg x 3 3/16" w. Single iron stamped "WILLIAM ASH & CO." Beech handle, wedge, and front knob. Brown and maroon with pin stripe decoration on each side.

Spotlight Plane

3

Goldsborough "Challenge" Planes

Inventor: Arthur T. Goldsborough

Origin: Washington, DC

Patent Number & Date:
284,732; September 11, 1883.

"Challenge" iron smooth plane (this page),
9" lg x 2 1/2" w. Handle and knob originally
painted black.

"Challenge" iron jack plane (at right)
15" lg x 2 3/4" w. Single iron 2 1/8" w.
Handle and knob painted black.
Sold by Tower & Lyon, New York, N.Y.
Cast into right side of plane
"CHALLENGE PAT. SEP.11.83 - FEB.19.84".

Munks & Son Smooth Plane

Inventor: John Munks & Son

Origin: Norfolk Works, Sheffield, England

Patent Number & Date:
(English) 1511; January 16, 1884.

Iron smooth plane 6 7/8" lg x 2" w. Unmarked single iron 1 3/4" w. Direct screw adjustment and handle design nearly identical to Goldsborough's Patented "Challenge" plane. Brass wing nut under the frog secures the cutter and adjustment mechanism.

Palmer
Bench Planes

Inventor: J. F. Palmer

Origin: Auburn, New York

Patent Number & Date: 16,569; February 3, 1857.

Beech smooth plane (left) 11 3/8" lg x 2 11/16" w. Patent stamped on toe. Patent assigned to S. W. Palmer, Detroit, Michigan.

Wood jack plane (below) 16 1/2" lg x 2 1/4" w. Toe stamped "T.J.M'MASTER & co. AUBURN, NY". Patent date stamped on cap iron. Plane incorporates Palmer's patented blade adjustment feature.

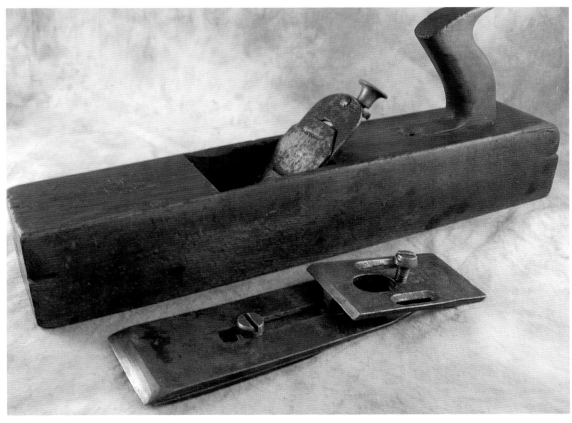

Longval Self Oiling Planes

Inventor: Oliver Longval

Origin: Millbury, Massachusetts

Patent Number & Date: 444,897; January 20, 1891.

Oliver Longval patent for two cup oilers
(under front knob and at the rear of the cutting iron).
Conversions made on a Stanley No. 8 plane.

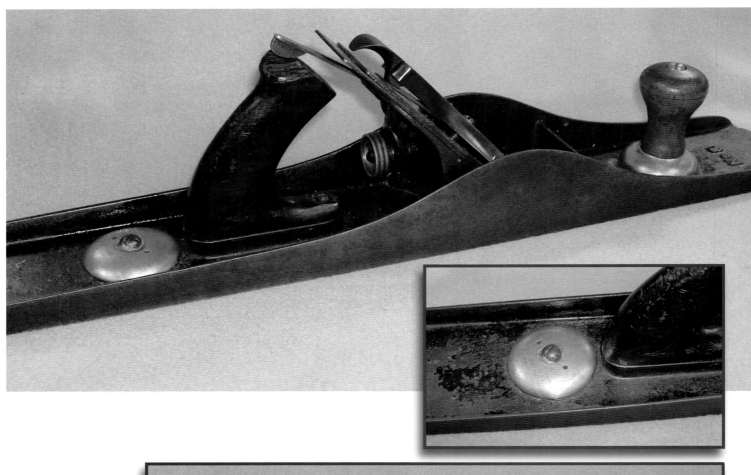

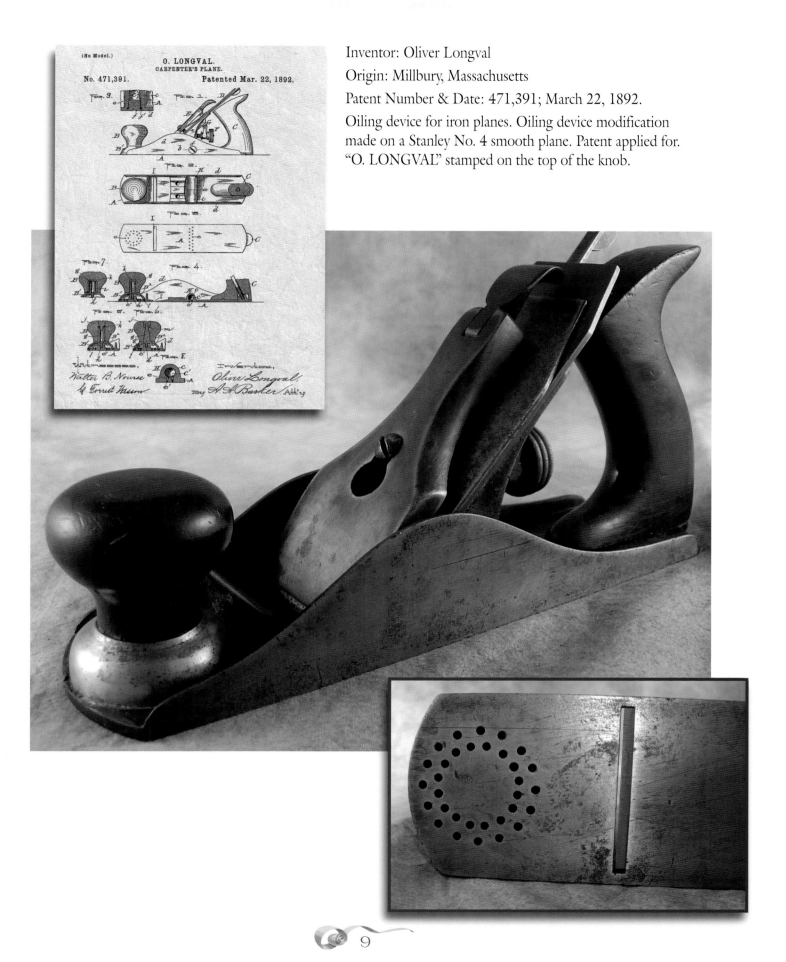

(No Model.)

O. LONGVAL.
CARPENTER'S PLANE.

No. 471,391.   Patented Mar. 22, 1892.

Inventor: Oliver Longval

Origin: Millbury, Massachusetts

Patent Number & Date: 471,391; March 22, 1892.

Oiling device for iron planes. Oiling device modification made on a Stanley No. 4 smooth plane. Patent applied for. "O. LONGVAL" stamped on the top of the knob.

Weyland
Self Oiling Plane

Inventor: Joseph Weyland

Origin: Los Angeles, California

Patent Number & Date:
770,881; September 27, 1904.

Self oiling plane modification. Fill hole at top of knob and dispensing hole on sole. Oiler feature modification made on a Stanley No. 4 1/2 plane.

Harris
Jointer Plane

Inventor: Horace Harris

Origin: Gorham, New York

Patent Number & Date: 13,575; September 18, 1855.

Jointer 22" lg x 3 1/8" w. Double iron 2 5/16" w.
Cap case 2 1/2" w. Patented adjustable iron stamped
"PATENTED No 4 SEPT 1855 WARRANTED"

Knowles Patent Planes

Inventor: Hazzard Knowles

Origin: Colchester, Connecticut

Patent Number & Date: Unknown.

Knowles type iron jointer 27" lg x 3 1/8 " w.
Double Iron, stamped "BUCK BROTHERS", 2 1/2" w.
herringbone pattern on bottom.

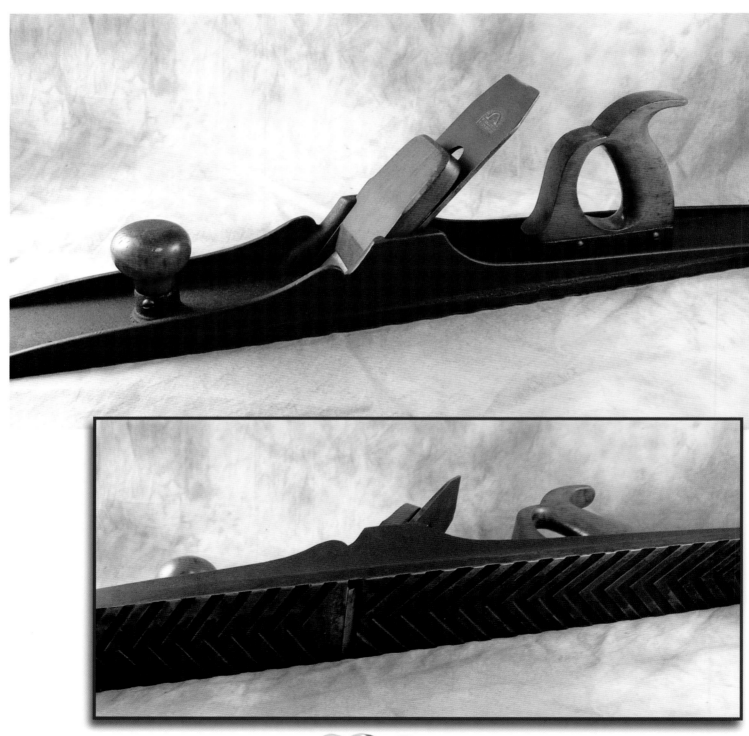

Inventor: Hazzard Knowles

Origin: Colchester, Connecticut

Patent Number & Date: Unknown.

Knowles Type Jack Plane 15" lg x 2 1/2" w. Single Iron 1 7/8" w. Wood wedge and open tote handle. Iron stamped "F. STONES".

Inventor: Hazzard Knowles

Origin: Colchester, Connecticut

Patent Number & Date: 34859X; August 24, 1827.

Iron Block Plane 7 5/8" lg x 3" w. Single iron stamped "CAM. & BROWN". Turned hickory knob. Cast iron receivers cast with bed indicate that this handle is probably original.

Maddox Rabbet Plane

Inventor: Edward Maddox

Origin: Victoria, Canada

Patent Number & Date: 496,267; April 25, 1893.

Iron rabbet plane 7 3/8" lg x 1" w. Single iron, unmarked. Iron frame, brass adjustment screw. Direct drive adjustment with cam lever to secure the iron. "NO. 3 PAT. APRIL 1893" stamped on toe.

Nordell Smooth Plane

Inventor: Carl Nordell

Origin: New York, New York

Patent Number & Date: 158,302;
December 29, 1874.

Iron smooth plane 11 1/2" lg x
2 5/16" w. Double iron 1 7/8" w.
No marks. Hardwood handle
& knob painted black.

Weaver Rabbet Plane

Inventor: George L. Weaver

Origin: Hartford, Connecticut

Patent Number & Date: 160,132;
February 23, 1875.

Iron rabbet plane. Walnut handle
and knob. 8" lg x 2 1/8" w. 2 1/8"
single iron, stamped
"MIDDLETOWN TOOL CO".

Holly Patent Planes

Inventor: Birdsill Holly

Origin: Seneca Falls, New York

Patent Number & Date: 9,904; July 6, 1852.

Iron jointer plane (below) 20 1/8" lg x 3 1/8" w. Double iron 2 1/2" w. marked "Casey, Kitchell & Co." Smooth bottom. Solid heavy cap iron with thumb screw that secures blade. Early Holly patented plane.

Iron jack plane (right) 15 7/15" lg x 2 9/16" w. Double iron 2 1/16" w., marked "GREAVES & SONS" Maple handle and knob. Metal "U" shaped clamp and thumb screw secure blade.

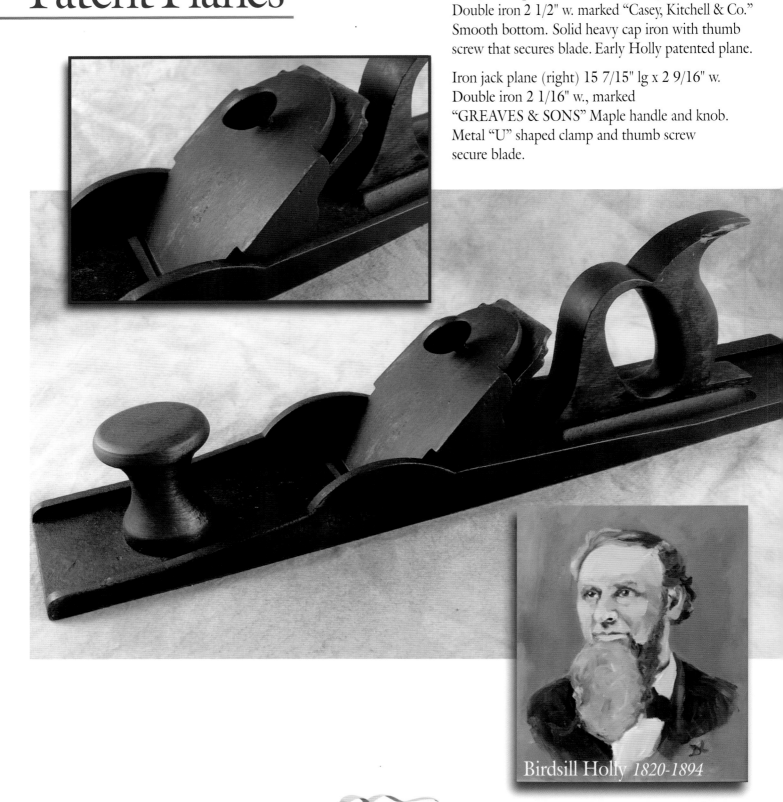

Birdsill Holly *1820-1894*

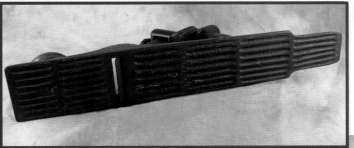

Holly
Patent Planes *Continued*

Inventor: Birdsill Holly

Origin: Seneca Falls, New York

Patent Number & Date: 9,904; July 6, 1852.

Smooth Plane 9 1/4" lg x 2 5/8" w.
Iron marked "MOULSON BROTHERS", 2 1/16"w.
Maple handle. Plane bottom has conical shaped
corrugations for reducing metal to wood friction.
A "U" shaped clamp and thumb screw
secure blade.

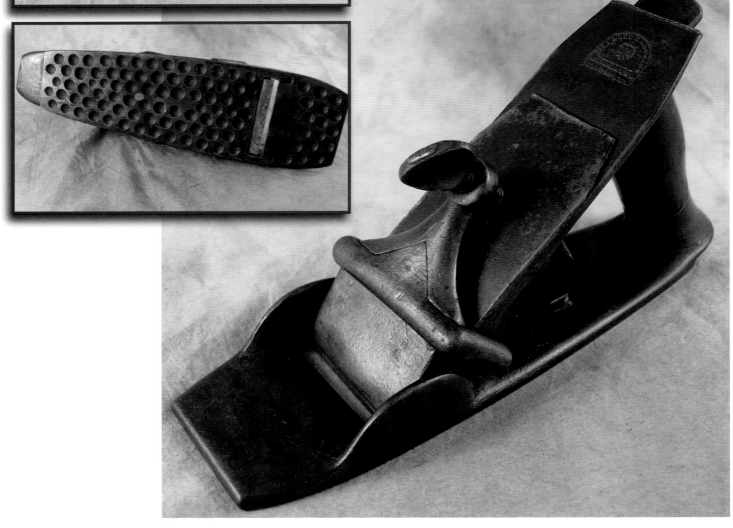

Inventor: Birdsill Holly

Origin: Seneca Falls, New York

Patent Number & Date: None Known.

Iron block plane 7 3/4" lg x 2" w. "Boat" shaped plane body with "shoe buckle" type cap. Single iron 1 3/4" w marked "BALDWIN TOOL CO. MADE FROM BUTCHER"S CAST STEEL WARRANTED" Turned maple knob. Small metal wedge inserted under blade helps secure cutting iron.

Sanford Planes

Inventor: Levi Sanford

Origin: East Solon, New York

Patent Number & Date:
3,838; November 26, 1844.

Wood smooth plane (right). Sanford's patent for blade adjustment feature likely fitted to conventional planes. 7 7/8" lg x 2 7/8" w.

Wood fore plane (below) 25 7/8" lg x 3 1/4" w. Double iron 2 3/4" w. Patent feature for blade mechanism. Patent stamped on blade adjustment mechanism. Toe stamped "L. SANFORD'S PATENT 1844".

Burlington Combination Plane

Inventor: Burkner F. Burlington

Origin: Wakefield, Massachusetts

Patent Number & Date: 151,682; June 9, 1874.

Combination clapboard block plane, marking gauge and square. One half of patent assigned to Joseph Cartwright. Burkner Burlington was a carpenter and Joseph Cartwright owned a hardware store in Wakefield, Massachusetts and probably provided financial backing.

Loughborough Patent Planes

Inventor: William Loughborough

Origin: Victor, New York

Patent Number & Date: 10,748; April 4, 1854.

Iron smooth plane (below), 10 3/4" lg x 2 1/16 w. Single iron 2" w, no marks. Two brass cap screws secures blade. Beech wood handle. "G & J TELFORD MAN'FRS ROCHESTER, NY" cast in body of plane. Manufactured by the G&J Telfords 1866 through 1868 only.

Smooth Plane (right), 13 1/2" lg. Cutter 2 1/8" w. Stamped "M. W. HOLLISTER ROCHESTER, NY." Earliest example of Loughborough's 1854 patent. "PATENT APPLIED FOR DIETRICH BROTHERS MANUFACTURERS ROCHESTER, N.Y." cast in plane bed at toe. Manufactured by Dietrich Brothers, Rochester, New York.

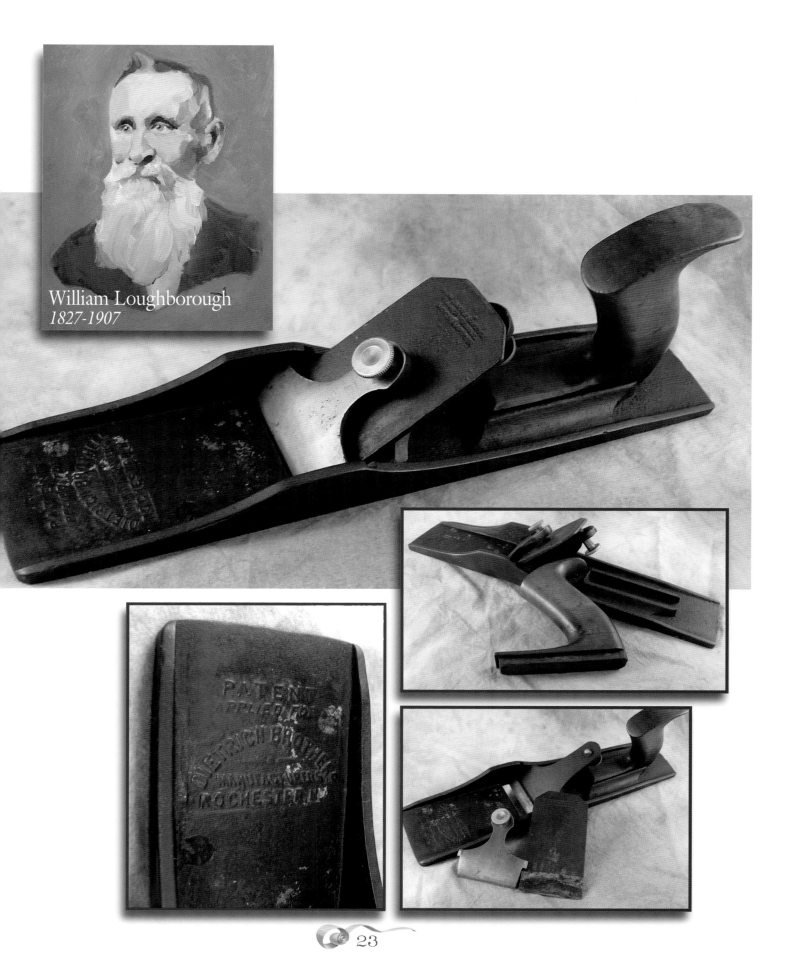

William Loughborough
1827-1907

PATENT
APPLIED FOR
DIETRICH BROWN
MANUFACTURER
ROCHESTER [?]

Loughborough Patent Planes *Continued*

Inventor: William Loughborough

Origin: Victor, New York

Patent Number & Date: 23,928; May 10, 1859.

Patent tongue plane. Iron frame 9 5/8" lg x 2 1/2" w. Single iron 2" w. Beech handle stamped "W. S. LOUGHBOROUGH, ROCHESTER, NY PATENT MAY 10, 1859". Adjustable iron fence. Tongue plane manufactured under Loughborough's filletster patent.

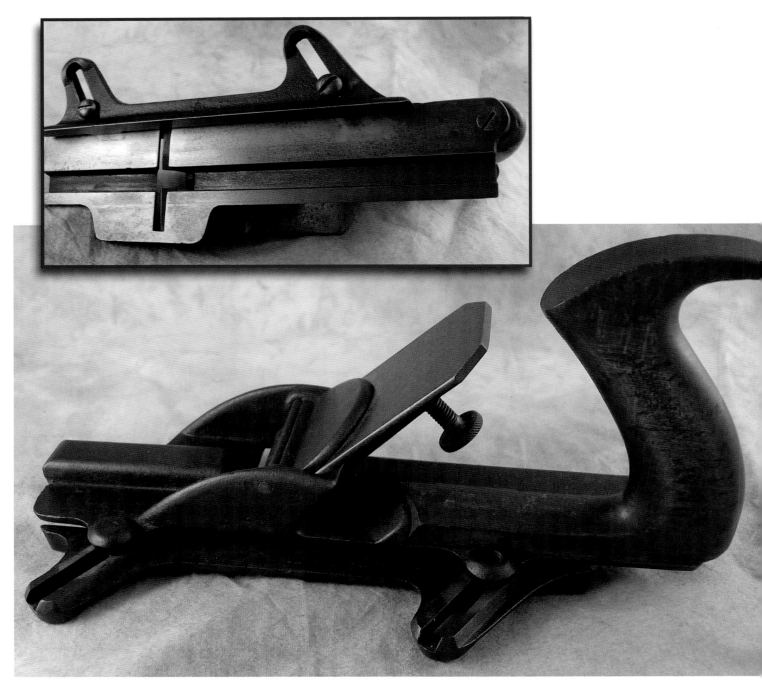

Shelabarger Smooth Plane

Inventor: Benjamin Shelabarger

Origin: Mifflintown, Pennsylvania

Patent Number & Date: 5,486;
March 28, 1848.

Beech smooth plane 7" lg x 2" w.
Double iron 1 7/8" w. Patent stamped on iron.
Manufacturer: J. Colton, Philadelphia.

Vaughn Smooth Plane

Inventor: Thomas Vaughn

Origin: Boston, Massachusetts

Patent Number & Date: 129,695;
July 23, 1872.

Beech smooth plane with a 9/16" thick
cast iron sole. 7 3/8" lg x 2 1/2" w.
Double iron 2 1/8" w, marked
"MOULSON BROTHERS
WARRANTED CAST STEEL".
Patent date stamped on toe.

Hayden Beveling Plane

Inventor: S. Hayden

Origin: Syracuse, New York

Patent Number & Date: Has Blye's Fence, Patent #6304; April 10, 1849.

Wood jack beveling plane 16" lg x 2 3/4" w. Iron 2 3/16" w, stamped "PROVIDENCE TOOL CO". Beech fence 16" lg x 2" w. Brass hinges and fittings. Toe stamped "HAYDEN, SYRACUSE, NY. W.H. BLYE PATENT APRIL 1849".

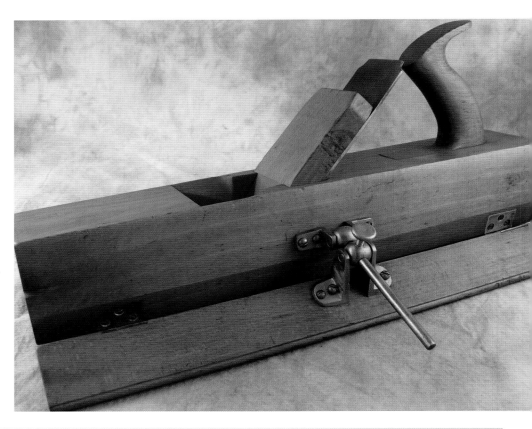

Ashley Block Plane

Inventor: Lewis C. Ashley

Origin: Troy, New York

Patent Number & Date: 14,436; March 18, 1856.

Block plane 8" lg x 2 7/16" w. Double iron stamped "MOULSON BROTHERS". "J.C. PATENTED FEB 1856" stamped on heel. A metal piece adjusts throat as plane bottom wears down.

Zoar
Fore Plane

Inventor: Zoar

Origin: Zoar, Ohio

Patent Number & Date: No Known Patent.

Fore plane 16" lg x 2 7/8" w. Iron stamped
"SANDUSKY TOOL CO WARRANTED".
Cap iron with thumb screw blade lock.
Open tote.

Boston Metallic Patent Planes

Inventor: Boston Metallic Plane Company

Origin: Boston, Massachusetts

Patent Number & Date: 131,544; September 24, 1872.

Jack plane with "slot-holes" in plane bottom covered by Cyrus H. Hardy's patent. This patent was assigned to Joseph F. Baldwin, Melina C. Patton & John Sully. Adjustment provision patented by Joseph Baldwin, patent #144,823, November 25, 1873. Patent assigned to John Sully. 15" lg. x 2 1/4" w. Decorated cap.

Maker: American Manufacturing Co.

Origin: Philadelphia, Pennsylvania

Patent Number & Date: 131,544; Sept 24, 1872.

Cyrus H. Hardy patent made by American
Manufacturing Company after Boston Metallic
Plane Co. closed its doors in 1874. Engraved cap
with floral design. Hardy's patent for holes in sole
assigned to Joseph Baldwin, Melina Patton
& John Sully. 9 1/2" lg x 2 3/8" w.

Boston Metallic Patent Planes *Continued*

Inventor: Boston Metallic Plane Company

Origin: Boston, Massachusetts

Patent Number & Date: 143,101; September 23, 1873.

Iron T- shaped rabbet plane 10 5/16" lg x 1 9/16" w. Beech handle, rosewood wedge. Patented by Francis Smith, Boston, Mass. Patent assigned to John Sully, Dedham, Mass. "BOSTON METALLIC PLANE CO." cast on side of plane frame.

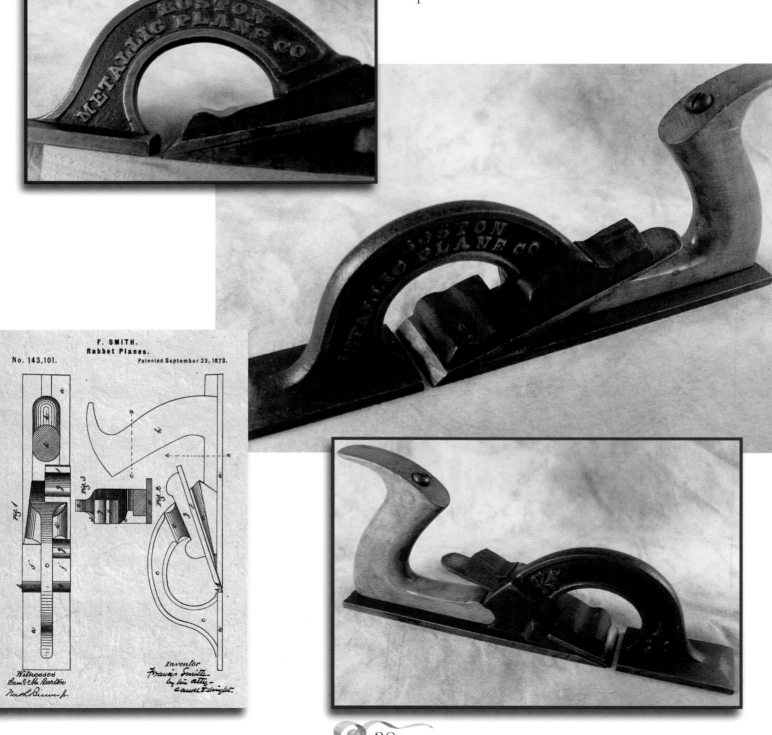

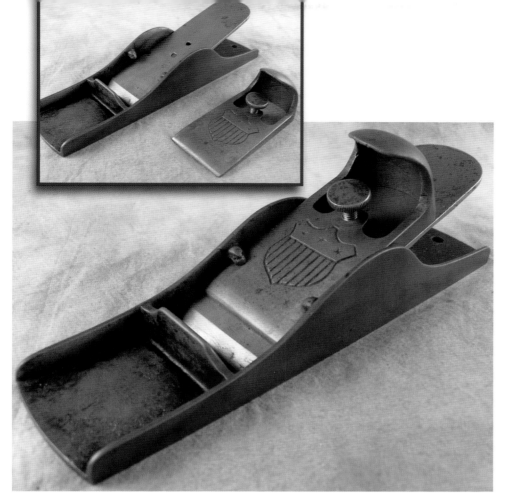

Inventor:
Boston Metallic Plane Company
Origin: Boston, Massachusetts
Patent Number & Date:
143,072; September 23, 1873.

Block plane (left), with a decorated cap "Stars & stripes" shield. Blade marked "BOSTON METALLIC PLANE CO." This is the long version block plane with Cyrus Hardy's patent. Patent assigned to John Sully of Dedhm, Massachusetts.

Iron block plane (below), "BOSTON METALLIC PLANE CO" stamped on wedge and cutter. 6 3/4" lg x 2" w. Cutter 1 1/2" w. Cap has palm rest. "BOSTON METALLIC PLANE CO." stamped on wood wedge and cutter.

Boston Metallic Patent Planes *Continued*

Inventor:
Boston Metallic Plane Company

Origin: Boston, Massachusetts

Patent Number & Date:
143,072; September 23, 1873

Iron block plane. Cap decorated with a floral design. Adjustable cutter. Top of blade is curved and connected to a threaded rod with a brass thumb screw. Blade adjustment made by turning thumb screw. Blade marked "AMERICAN MFG. CO. PHILA.".

Inventor: A. L. Whiting & Company

Origin: Boston, Massachusetts

Patent Number & Date: None known

Boston Metallic Plane Company style block plane 6" lg x 1 7/8" w.
Blade stamped "A.L WHITING & CO"
1 5/8" wide. Wood wedge.

Inventor: Boston Metallic Plane Company

Origin: Boston, Massachusetts

Patent Number & Date:
143,072; September 23, 1873

Metal non-adjustable block plane. No palm rest. Raised "rib" feature in front of plane mouth is higher than most Boston Metallic Plane Company's block planes. Both iron and wood blade marked "BOSTON METALLIC PLANE CO."

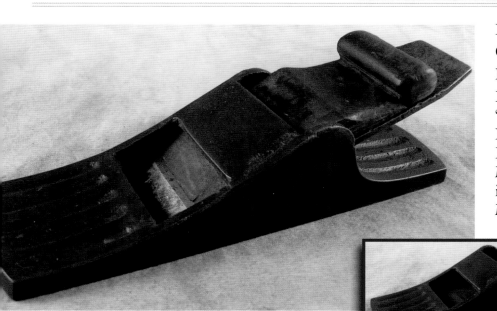

Inventor: Boston Metallic Plane Company

Origin: Boston, Massachusetts

Patent Number & Date: None Known

Block plane 7" lg. Blade marked "BOSTON METALLIC PLANE CO." Heavy rib pattern on top side of plane. Blade is locked in place by a wood wedge. Metal support piece that connects plane sides is wider than those normally seen on Boston Metallic Plane Company block planes.

Boston Metallic Patent Planes *Continued*

Inventor: Boston Metallic Plane Company

Origin: Boston, Massachusetts

Patent Number & Date: 131,544; September 24, 1872.

Cyrus Hardy patent (Boston Metallic Plane Company), 14 3/4" lg. x 2 1/2" w. Plane sold by American Manufacturing Company after the Boston Metallic Plane Company closed in 1874. Cyrus Hardy patent is for holes in plane sole. Patent assigned to Joseph Baldwin, Melina C. Patton and John Sully.

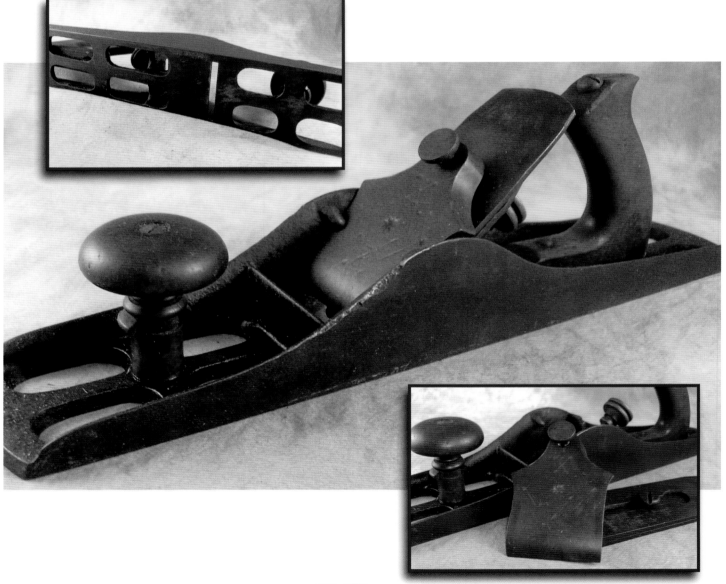

Tidey
Jack Plane

Inventor: M. B. Tidey

Origin: Ithaca, New York

Patent Number & Date: 16,889; March 24, 1867.

Beech jack plane 15 7/8" lg x 2 3/4" w. Double iron 2" w.
Marked "M.B. TIDEY & CO. DUNDEE, N.Y."
Toe stamped "M.B. TIDEY ITHACA"

Gladwin
Patent Planes

Inventor: Porter A, Gladwin

Origin: Boston, Massachusetts

Patent Number & Date: 185,442; December 19, 1876.

Adjustable combination plane 11 3/8" lg x 3 1/8" w. including fence. P. A. Gladwin patent stamped on toe. "PAT DEC 19 1876" Irons sharpened on both ends.

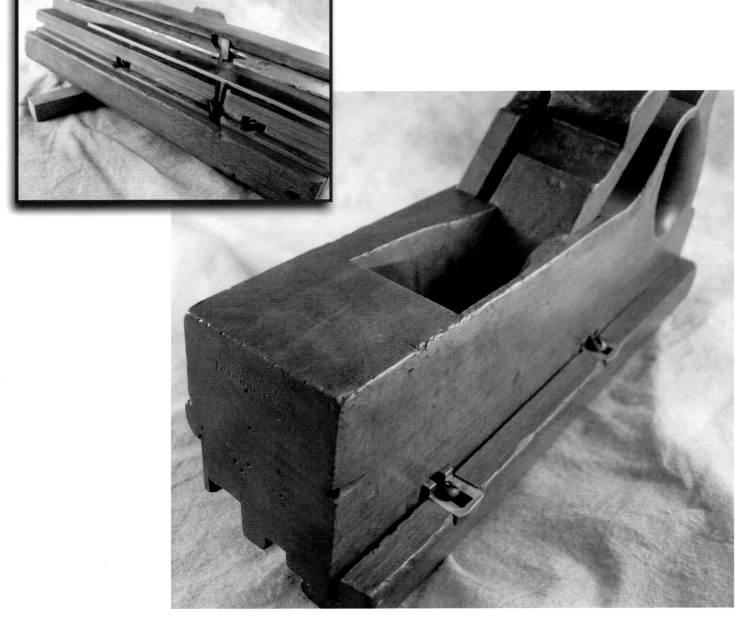

Inventor: Porter A. Gladwin

Origin: Boston, Massachusetts

Patent Number & Date:
17,451; June 9, 1857.

Porter A, Gladwin handled combination match plane (left), for making tongue and grooves. Beech 11 1/2" lg x 2 1/4" w. Two irons and wedges side by side. Patent assigned to P.A. Gladwin and Thomas F. Caldicott. Toe marked "P. A. GLADWIN CO. PATENTED JUNE 9, 1857".

Razee handled combination match plane (below), for making tongue and grooves. Two irons and wedges side by side. 11 3/8" lg x 2 3/8" w. Plane shorter than most known P.A Gladwin's patented combination planes. Toe marked "THOS APPLETON BOSTON"

Gladwin
Patent Planes *Continued*

Inventor: Porter A, Gladwin

Origin: Boston, Massachusetts

Patent Number & Date: 19,359; February 16, 1858.

Beech smooth plane 11" lg. x 3 5/16" w.

Double iron 2 5/8" w. marked "William Ash & Co".

"J.R. Marr" stamped on toe. Only one presently known.

Bee
Bench Plane

Inventor: Benjamin F. Bee

Origin: Harwich, Massachusetts

Patent Number & Date: 8,503; November 11, 1851.

"GEO. BURNHAM AMHERST, MASS" Stamped on toe.
"B.F. Bee's" patent stamped on pewter disc attached to side.

Norwood
Patent Planes

Inventor: John E. Norwood

Origin: Boston, Massachusetts

Patent Number & Date: 161,701; April 6, 1875.

Iron rabbet block plane 7 5/16" lg x 1 3/4" w.
Single iron 1 3/4" w. Dated "APRIL 6, 1875" on side.
Patent specs do not show an adjustment feature but all
known planes of Norwood's design have adjustable feature
similar to L. Leonard Bailey's June 22, 1858 patent.

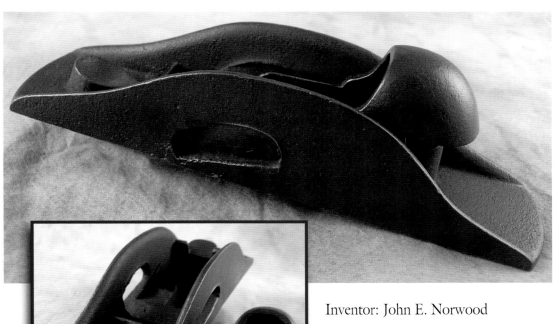

Inventor: John E. Norwood

Origin: Boston, Massachusetts

Patent Number & Date: 161,701; April 6, 1875.

John E. Norwood patent iron rabbet block plane; casting only. Casting lacks "nibs" for blade cap locks. No throat opening.

Inventor: John E. Norwood

Origin: Boston, Massachusetts

Patent Number & Date: None known.

A John E. Norwood casting of an unfinished block plane. A prototype experimental design plane body.

Norwood
Patent Planes *Continued*

Inventor: John E. Norwood

Origin: Boston, Massachusetts

Patent Number & Date: None known.

Iron rabbet plane 9 5/8" x 2 3/8". Sinlge iron stamped "PAT. APRIL 6, 1875". Plane has lever lock detachable handle. Handle is secured by two "prongs" extending from handle over a screw post in plane base. Handle is secured by pulling up lever.

Stoddard
Jack Plane

Inventor: William Stoddard

Origin: Lowell, Massachusetts

Patent Number & Date: 17,645;
June 23, 1857.

Beech jack plane 15 15/16" lg x
2 3/16" w. Double iron 1 15/16" w,
marked "WILLIAM ASH".
"PAT JUNE 23 1857 M STODDARD"
stamped on cam lever.

Doll
Jack Plane

Inventor: August Doll

Origin: Lena, Illinois

Patent Number & Date: 334,943;
Janaury 26, 1886.

Beech jack plane 15 1/4" lg x 2 3/4" w.
Double iron 2 1/4" w. No marks.
Beech handle and knob.

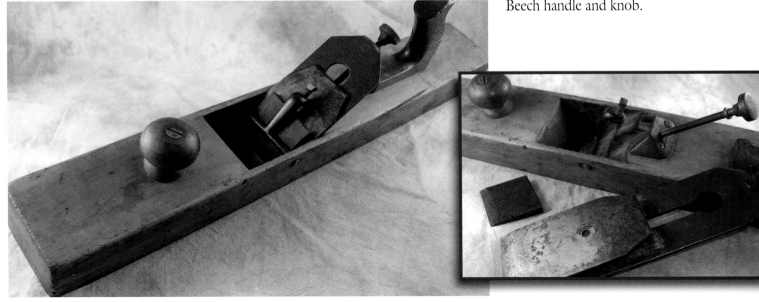

Lee Chamfer Plane

Inventor: Joseph Lee

Origin: Garnerville, New York

Patent Number & Date: 272,274; February 13, 1883.

Lee's patent stop chamfer plane. Iron frame & fence. Double iron. Mahogany handle. Black japanned finish on frame and fence. Gothic window design. Plane manufactured by "Horace Thurston, Providence, RI." This is the rare variation with a "Bailey type" lever cap and his 1867 patented adjustment feature.

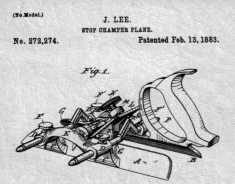

(No Model.)

J. LEE.
STOP CHAMFER PLANE.

No. 272,274.   Patented Feb. 13, 1883.

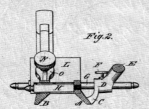

Spotlight Plane

Morris
Patent Planes

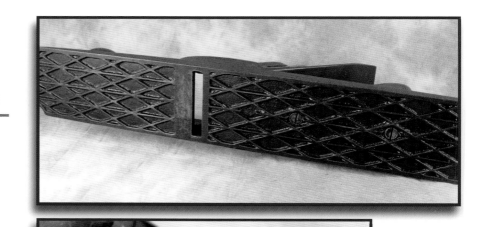

Inventor: Ellis H. Morris

Origin: Salem, Ohio

Patent Number & Date:
109,037; November 8, 1870.

Iron jointer plane 21 5/8" lg x 3 1/16" w.
Double iron 2 5/16" w, stamped
"BUCK BROS. WARRANTED."
Wood handle wedge and knob.
Patent "NOV 8 1870" cast on bed near
mouth. Manufactured by Sandusky
Tool Company 1870-1875.

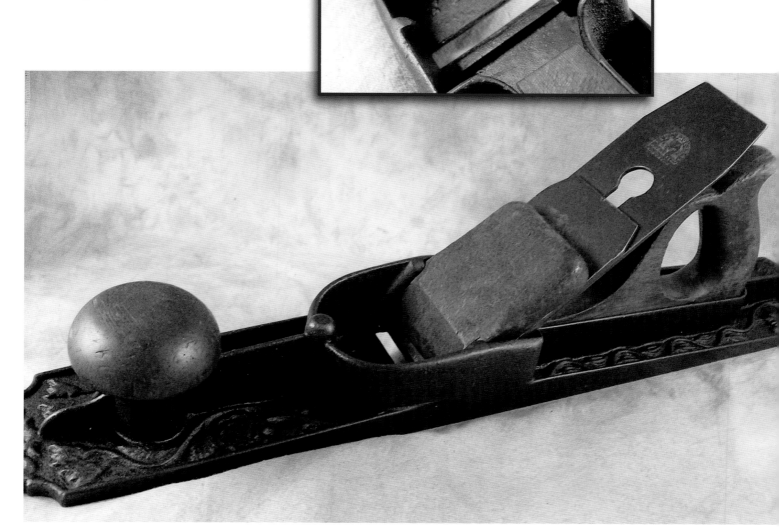

Inventor: Ellis H. Morris

Origin: Salem, Ohio

Patent Number & Date:
109,037; November 8, 1870.

Iron jack plane 15 3/4" lg x 2 9/16" w. 2 1/4"
Double iron marked "BALDWIN TOOL CO
WARRANTED". Patent cast on bed near
mouth "PAT'D NOV 8 1870". Wood
wedge, handle and knob. Manufactured by
Sandusky Tool Company Salem, Ohio.

Morris
Patent Planes *Continued*

Inventor: Ellis H. Morris

Origin: Salem, Ohio

Patent Number & Date: 109,037; November 8, 1870.

Morris Patent iron smooth plane 10" lg x 2 1/4" w.
Double iron stamped "SANDUSKY TOOL CO."
"PATD APL FOR" cast in plane body bottom under handle.
The word "BOSS" is cast in plane body toe by knob receiver.

Blye Beveling Planes

Inventor: W. H. Blye

Origin: DeRuyter, New York

Patent Number & Date:
6,304; April 10, 1849.

Beveling plane (left) 9 1/2" lg x 2" w. Unmarked. Brass hinges and fittings. Toe stamped "E.C. RING, RINGVILLE, MS." Not marked with patent date but unmistakable Blye Patent.

Beveling plane (below) 9 1/2" lg x 2" w. Beech fence 9 1/2" lg. Brass hinges and fittings. Toe stamped "HAYDEN, Syracuse, N.Y," "W.H. BLYE'S PATENT APRIL 1849". Hammer in hand logo also on toe.

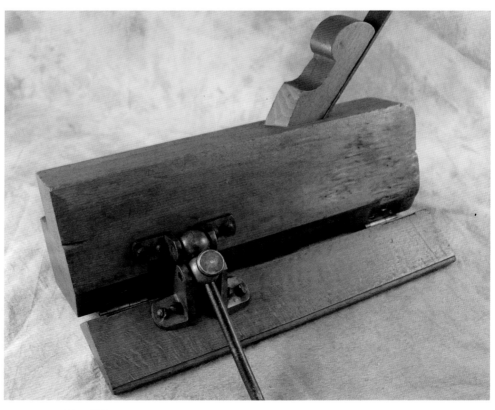

Foss
Patent Planes

Inventor: Henry A. Foss

Origin: New Britain, Connecticut

Patent Number & Date: Two assigned (see below).

Iron smooth plane 8 1/4" lg x 2" w. Double iron 1 1/4" w.
Adjustable model. Lever cap patent #207,599;
September 3, 1878. Cutter adjustment patent #186,996;
February 6, 1877. Foss patent stamped on adjustment nut.

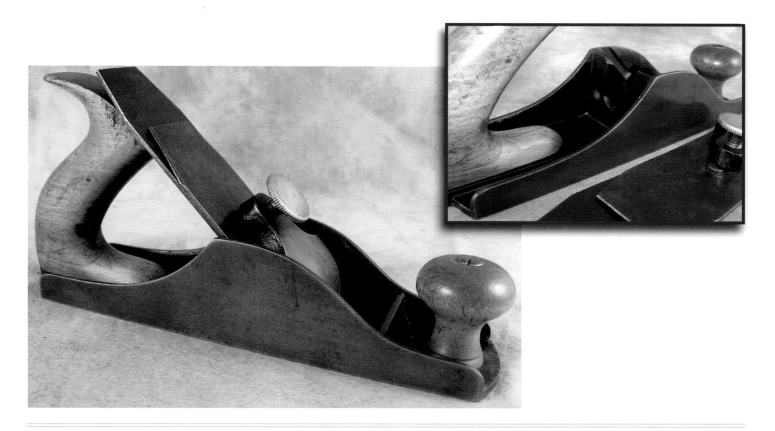

Inventor: Henry A. Foss

Origin: Pine Meadow, Connecticut

Patent Number & Date:
207,599; September 3, 1878.

Non-adjustable plane (above),
8 1/4" lg x 2" w. Double iron 1 3/4" w,
no marks. Beech handle and knob.
Assigned to Philip E. Chapin.

Smooth plane (right), with Foss'
patented cap iron. Non-adjustable
model. Wood handle and knob.
Plated screw cap lock. 8" lg x 2" w.
Unmarked double iron 1 3/4" w.

Foss
Patent Planes *Continued*

Inventor: Henry A. Foss

Origin: Pine Meadow, Connecticut

Patent Number & Date: 207,599; September 3, 1878.

Foss' Patent No. 1 non-adjustable iron block plane
6 1/4" lg. x 1 13/16" w. Single iron unmarked. Rosewood front
knob and grip knob. Manufactured by Henry A. Foss and
Philip E. Chapin at the Chapin factory in Pine Medow, Connecticut.

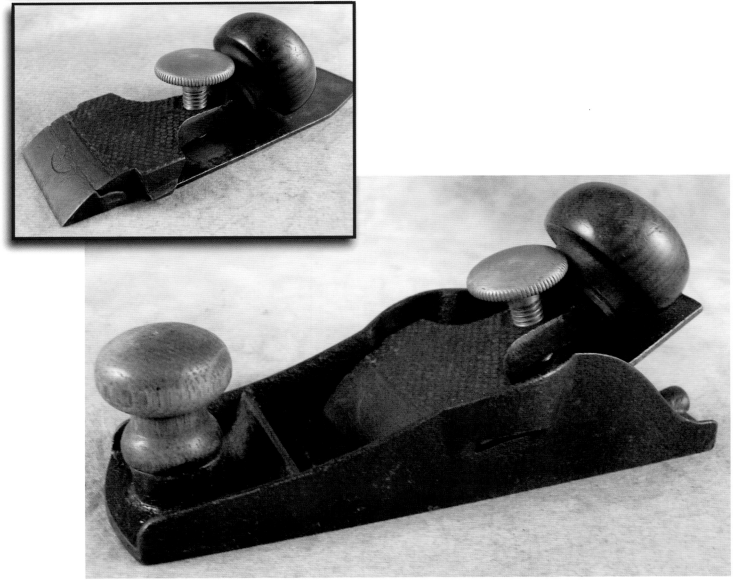

Phillips Jointer Plane

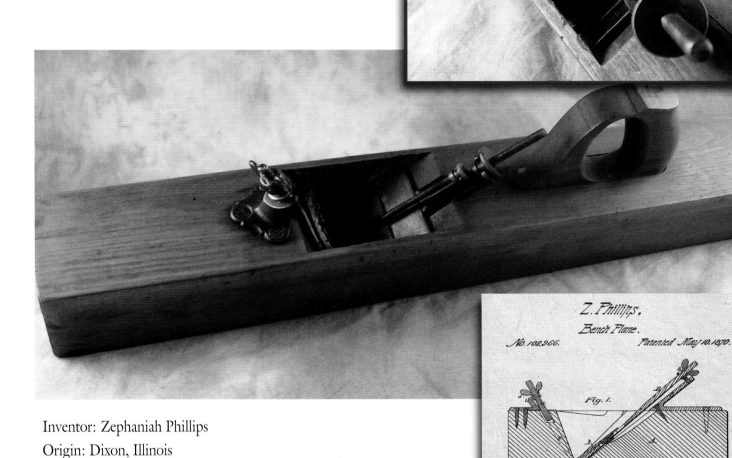

Inventor: Zephaniah Phillips

Origin: Dixon, Illinois

Patent Number & Date: 102,966; May 10, 1870.

Beech jointer plane 22" lg x 3" w.
Double iron "Z PHILLIPS PAT 1870" cast on throat.

Steers Patent Planes

Inventor: William Steers

Origin: Sherbrooke, Quebec, Canada

Patent Number & Date: 284,919; September 11, 1883.

Iron fore plane (below), 17 5/8" lg x 2 5/8" w.
Single iron 2 1/4" w, marked "STEERS PAT. NO. 306".
Rosewood handle and knob. Rosewood strips dovetailed
to sole. Sold by J.E. Jennings & Co., New York.

Iron smooth plane (right page), 9 1/8" lg x 2 5/16" w.
2" single iron. Stamped "STEERS PATENT" & "NO 304".
Rosewood strips dovetailed to sole.

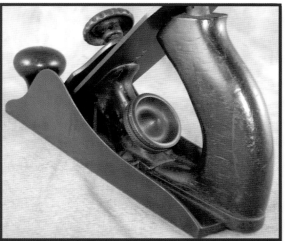

Steers
Patent Planes *Continued*

Inventor: William B. Steers

Origin: Brattleboro, Vermont

Patent Number & Date: 310,473; January 6, 1885.

Iron smooth plane 9" lg x 2" w. Single iron 1 3/4" w. Marked with Steer's patent and "No. 403". Rosewood handle and knob. No rosewood strips in sole.

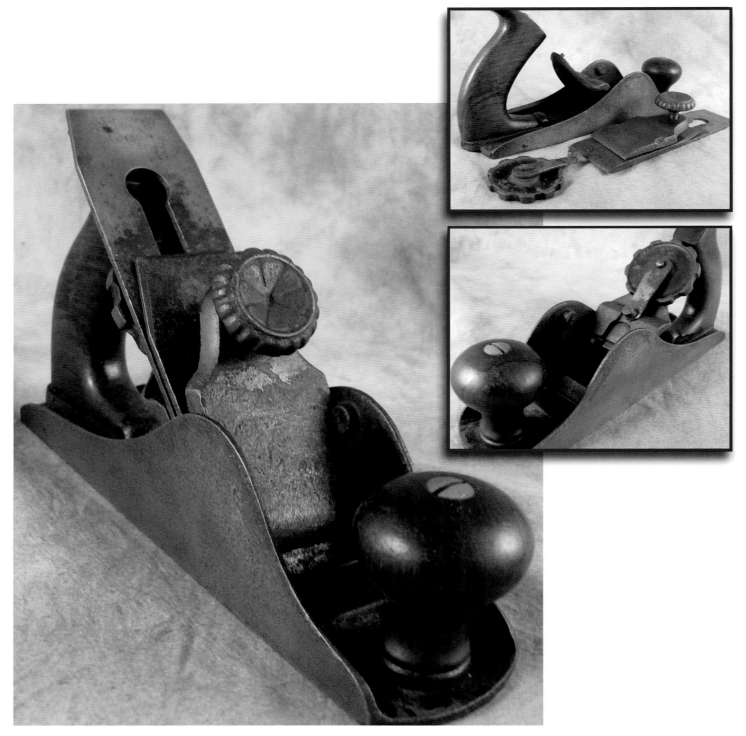

Inventor: C. E. Jennings Company

Origin: New York, New York.

Patent Number & Date: Circa 1890.

Smooth plane. Bailey type cutter adjustment.
No lateral adjuster. Marked Jennings with Steers
patent (1883). Very possible that this plane was
made by Brattleboro Tool Co. & Jennings acquired
this company after it ceased operations in 1887.

Steers Patent Planes *Continued*

Inventor: William Steers

Origin: Brattleboro, Vermont

Patent Number & Date:
310,473; January 6, 1885.

Non-adjustable iron block plane 7" lg. x 1 7/8" w. Single iron blade 1 9/16" w. stamped "BRATTLEBORO TOOL CO."

Inventor: Brattleboro Tool Company

Origin: Brattleboro, Vermont

Patent Number & Date:
None Known.

Non-adjustable iron block plane. Single Iron 1 3/4" w. stamped "BRATTLEBORO TOOL CO." 5 1/4" lg x 1 5/8" w.

Boyce
Smooth Plane

Inventor: Joseph B. Boyce

Origin: Lockport, New York

Patent Number & Date: 199,956; February 5, 1878.

Wood smooth plane equipped with cast iron throat piece. 8" lg X 2 5/8" w. Double iron 2" w. "GREENFIELD TOOL GREENFIELD MASS" stamped on toe.

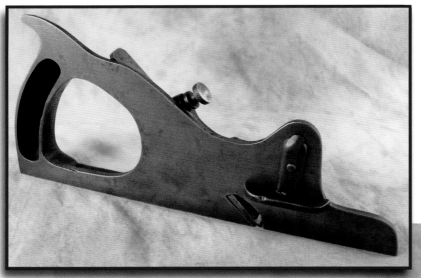

Tatum
Rabbet Plane

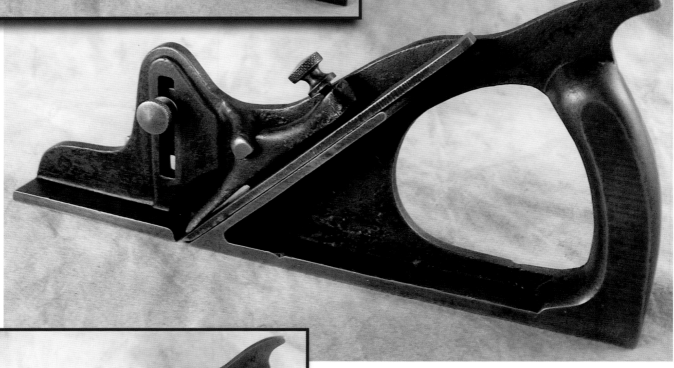

Inventor: S.C. Tatum & Co.

Origin: Green Island, New York

Patent Numbers & Dates - 3 Patent Numbers:
John M. Bennett, Green Island, New York, #284,941, September 11, 1883;
Samuel E. Hilles, Cincinnati, Ohio, #299,927, June 3, 1884;
A. Keiser, Cincinnati, Ohio, #305,602, September 23, 1884.

Iron rabbet plane. Hilles and Keiser apparently worked for S.C. Tatum & Co. Stamped on side of handle "PAT. SEP. 11 '83".

Gaylord Plough Plane

(No Model.)

E. L. GAYLORD.
PLANE FOR PICTURE MOLDINGS.

No. 313,195.   Patented Mar. 3, 1885.

Fig 1

Fig 2

Witnesses
S. Williamson
W. J. Manland

Inventor
Edward L. Gaylord
By Smith & Hubbard
Attys.

Inventor: Edward L. Gaylord
Origin: Bridgeport, Connecticut
Patent Number & Date: 313,195; March 3, 1885.
S10" lg x 1 1/4" w. Rosewood handle.
Interchangeable soles. No marks. Special plane for
picture moldings. Iron frame.

Jones
Shoot Board Plane

Inventor: Joseph Jones

Origin: Newark, New Jersey

Patent Number & Date:
52,719; February 20, 1866.

J. Jones shoot board plane. Beech plane.
Board iron top with cherry base 7" x 18" overall.
Single iron stamped "W BUTCHER".
"JONES PATENT FEB. 20, 1866" stamped on
brass nameplate. Toe stamped "MO" stamped
in four places on the plane.

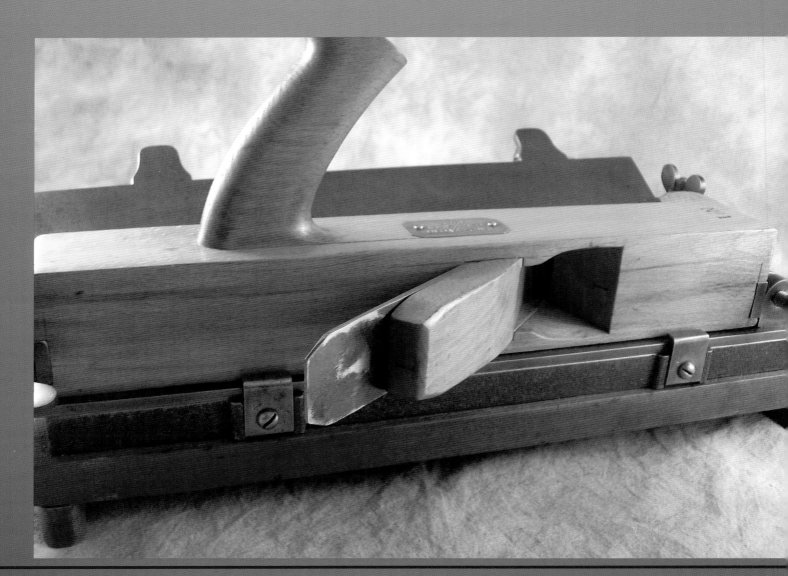

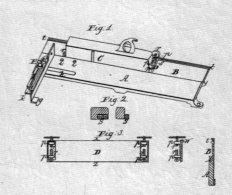

J. Jones,
Shooting Board,
Nº 52,719.   Patented Feb. 20, 1866.

Fig. 1.

Fig. 2.

Fig. 3.

Fig. 4.

Witnesses;
Chas. H. Kremer
William Martin

Inventor;
Joseph Jones.

Spotlight Plane

L. Bailey
Patent Planes

Inventor: Leonard Bailey

Origin: Winchester, Massachusetts

Patent Numbers & Dates:
20,615; June 22, 1858 & 21,311; August 31, 1858.

Beech jointer 26" lg x 3 1/2" w. with Bailey lever cap & patented adjustment feature. Double iron stamped "MOULSON BROTHERS" "H.H. CLEVELAND-BOSTON BAILEY'S PATENT AUG 31, 1858" stamped on toe.

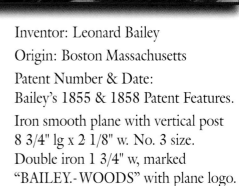

Inventor: Leonard Bailey

Origin: Boston Massachusetts

Patent Number & Date:
Bailey's 1855 & 1858 Patent Features.

Iron smooth plane with vertical post
8 3/4" lg x 2 1/8" w. No. 3 size.
Double iron 1 3/4" w, marked
"BAILEY.-WOODS" with plane logo.
Rosewood handle and knob.

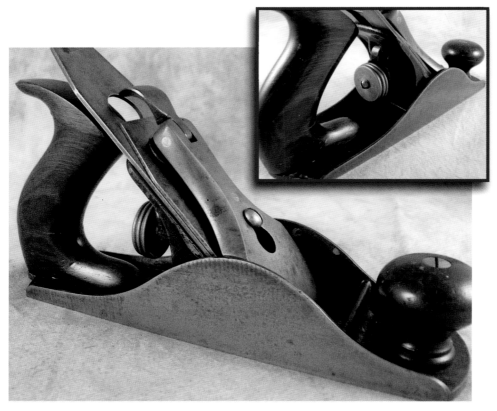

Inventor: Leonard Bailey

Origin: Boston, Massachusetts

Patent Number & Date:
Bailey's 1858 & 1867 Patent Features.

Iron smooth plane 8 3/4" lg x 2 1/8" w.
Double iron 1 3/4" w. Stamped
"DEC. 24, 1867". Brass adjustment
nut stamped "BAILEY & CO".
Traces of name "WOODS" remaining.
Rosewood handle and knob.

L. Bailey
Patent Planes *Continued*

Inventor: Leonard Bailey

Origin: Winchester, Massachusetts

Patent Number & Date:
13,381; 1855 & 21,311; 1858.

Iron jack plane 13 1/2" lg x 2 3/8" w.
Double iron 2" w, stamped
"MOULSON BROTHERS".
Split frame with lever cap. Rosewood
handle and knob. "BAILEY'S PAT.-
AUG 7, 1855" stamped on front knob.

Inventor: Leonard Bailey

Origin: Boston, Massachusetts

Patent Number & Date:
Bailey's 1858 & 1867
Patent Features.

Wood bottom smooth plane.
9 1/2" lg. x 2 1/4" w. Iron 1 3/4" w.
Solid brass adjustment nut -
has traces of the name "WOODS"
on brass nut. Type 1 No. 25 size.

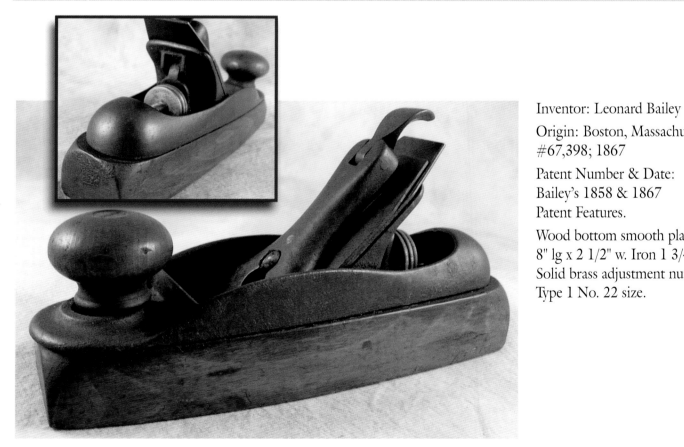

Inventor: Leonard Bailey

Origin: Boston, Massachusetts
#67,398; 1867

Patent Number & Date:
Bailey's 1858 & 1867
Patent Features.

Wood bottom smooth plane
8" lg x 2 1/2" w. Iron 1 3/4" w.
Solid brass adjustment nut.
Type 1 No. 22 size.

L. Bailey
Patent Planes *Continued*

Inventor: Leonard Bailey

Origin: Boston, Massachusetts

Patent Number & Date:
Bailey's 1858 & 1867 Patent Features.

Wood bottom "Jenny" plane 12 5/8" lg x 3 1/4" w.
Iron 2 1/2" w. Solid brass adjustment knob.
Type 1 No. 37 size.

Inventor: Stanley Rule & Level Company

Origin: New Britain, Connecticut

Patent Number & Date: 20,614; August 31, 1858.

Block Plane Stanley Rule & Level Company No. 9 3/4.
6 1/4" lg x 1 7/8" w. Single iron 1 5/8" w. Leonard Bailey
patent August 31, 1858. Lever adjustment for cutter
is under Bailey's second patent, #20,614;
June 22, 1858. Plane offered in 1873 and 1875 only.

L. Bailey
Patent Planes *Continued*

Inventor: Leonard Bailey

Origin: Winchester, Massachsetts

Patent Number & Date: April 7, 1858.

Early L. Bailey experimental plane. Rosewood handle and front cross piece. Iron base has a series of holes drilled through the sides. The two long pins can be alternated in the holes to a regular pitch or vertical for scraping. One pin is the pivot for the frog the other acts as a fulcrum to secure the lever cap. 9 " lg. x 2 5/32" w.

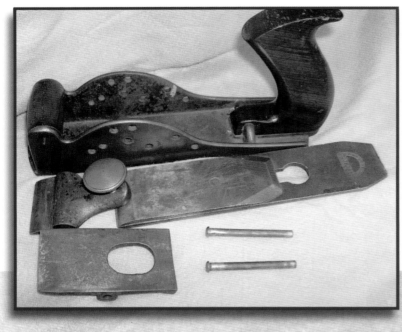

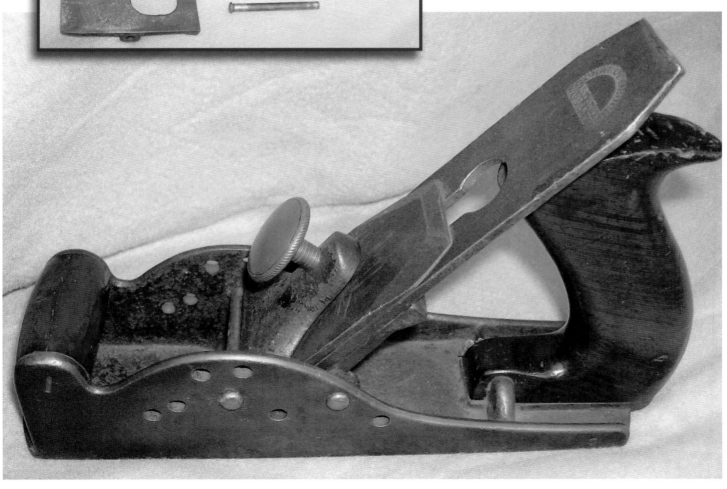

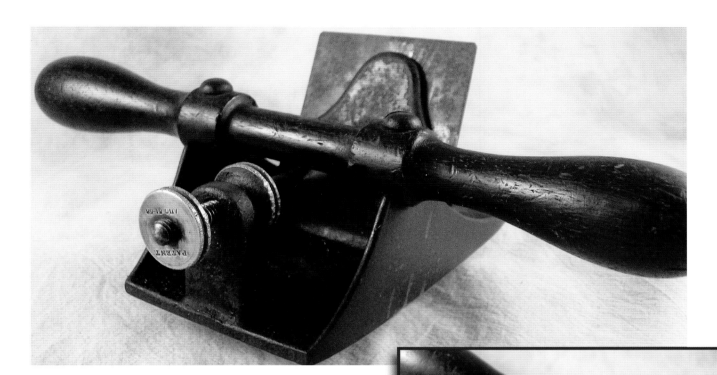

Inventor: Leonard Bailey

Origin: Winchester, , Massachusetts

Patent Number & Date: 13,381; August 7, 1855.

Bailey's No. 12 Scraper Plane. Type 1 model. Single iron. Rosewood handles. "PATENT AUG 31- 58" stamped on brass adjustment nut. Bailey's patent No. 13,381 August 7, 1855.

Meriden Patent Planes

Inventor: Meriden Malleable Iron Company

Origin: Middletown, Connecticut

Patent Number & Date:
257,981; May 16, 1882 &
289,332; November 27, 1883

Iron block plane; early version, adjustable throat.
8" lg x 1 3/4" w. Iron marked "MERIDEN
MAL IRON COMPANY PATENTED".
Solon Rust 1882 patent, William Tidgewell 1883 patent.

Inventor: Meriden Malleable Iron

Origin: Meriden, Connecticut

Patent Number & Date: Several Patents.

Iron fore plane 17 7/8" lg x 2 7/8" w. Solon Rust Patent and others. Brass adjustment nut stamped "Patent May 16, 1882; November 20, 1883; November 27, 1883".

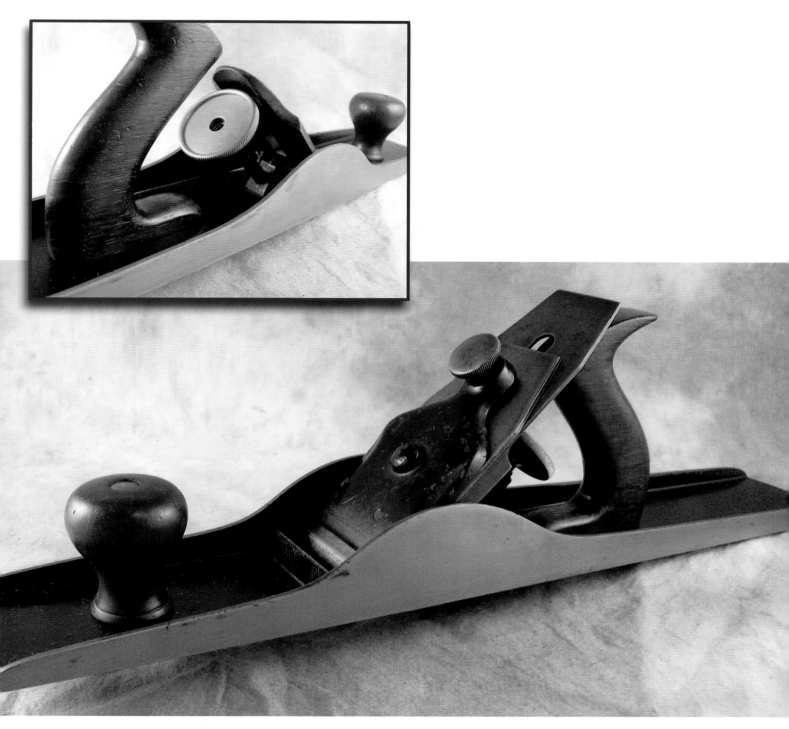

Meriden Patent Planes *Continued*

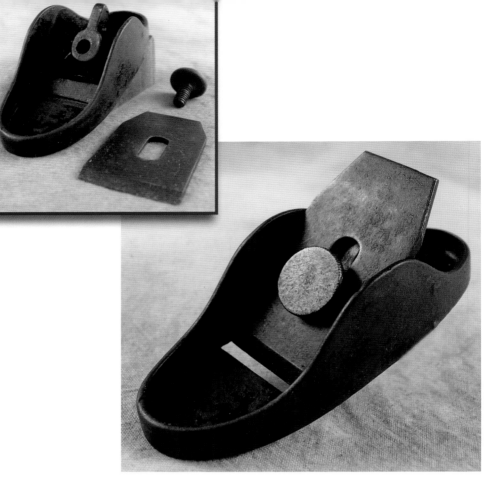

Inventor:

Meriden Patent Novelty Company

Origin: Meriden, Connecticut

Patent Number & Date: Circa 1883.

Toy size iron block plane 3" lg x 1 1/4" w. "Boat" shape body; single iron; thumb screw blade lock.

Inventor: Meriden Patent Novelty Company

Origin: Meriden, Connecticut

Patent Number & Date:
(Solon Rust patent) 282,468; July 31, 1883.

Toy size iron block plane 4 11/16" lg x 1 1/2" w. Cap iron with palm rest. Single iron marked "MERIDEN PATENT NOVELTY CO"

Lovejoy Smooth Plane

Inventor: D. Lovejoy & Son

Origin: Lowell, Massachusetts

Patent Number & Date: No known Patent.

Iron smooth plane 9 3/8" lg x 2 1/4" w. Skewed single iron 3/16" thick x 2 1/4" w. Cherry handle and front knob. Blade stamped "D. LOVEJOY & SON LOWELL MASS".

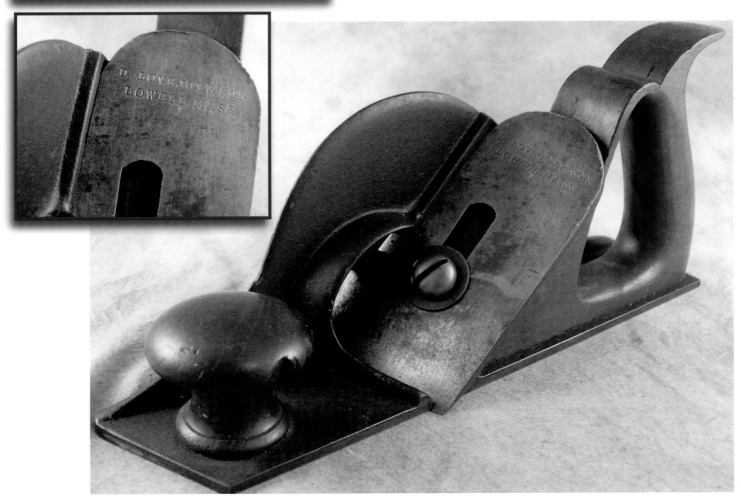

Spencer Smooth Plane

Inventor: J. Ceville Spencer

Origin: Phelps, New York

Patent Number & Date:
138,591; May 6, 1873.

Beech smooth plane 8 1/4" lg x 2 1/2" w.
Double iron. "A. HOWLAND & CO."
stamped on toe. Patent date on brass wheel.

Phelps Combination Plane

Inventor: Phelps

Origin: Auburn Tool Co., Auburn, New York

Patent Number & Date: None known

Phelps combination plane 16" lg x 2 1/2" w.
double iron 2 1/4" w. A level glass is set on the
left side and measures 1 through 16 inches
on lower left edge. Circa 1890. Toe marked
"AUBURN TOOL Co. AUBURN NY".

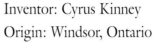

Kinney Gauge Ripping Plane

Inventor: Cyrus Kinney

Origin: Windsor, Ontario

Patent Number & Date: No known patent.

Gauge ripping plane 11 1/4" lg x 2 1/8" w. Rotary cutter.
Steel fence arm 9 3/4" lg. "SANDUSKY TOOL CO."
in a "flying banner" stamped on toe. Plane circa 1885 and
advertised as Kinney patent; however, no patent known.

Jones Scraper Plane

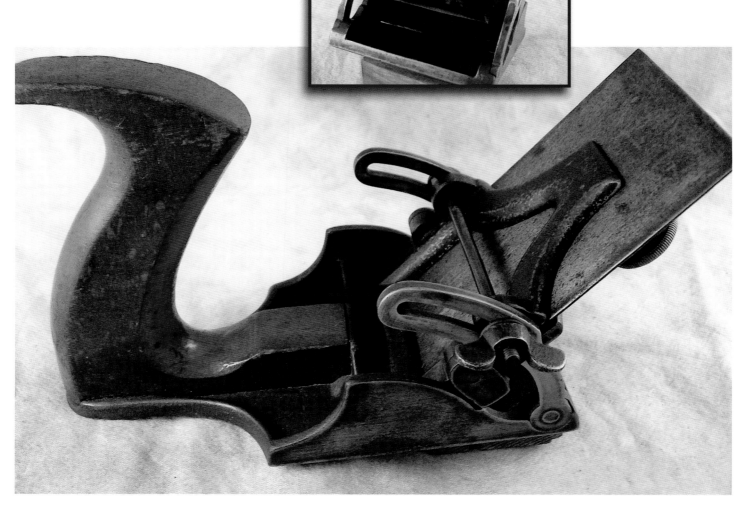

Inventor: Joseph Jones

Origin: Newark, New Jersey

Patent Number & Date: 135,341; January 28, 1873.

Scraper plane with brass arms and cap screw.
6 1/16" lg x 3 1/4" w. Single cutter. Assigned to
William A. Freeman. Patent date stamped on right
brass arm "SEP. 24, 1872".

Brooks Tongue & Groove Plane

Inventor: P. Brooks

Origin: Possibly Williamstown, Massachusetts

Patent Number & Date: No known patent.

Tongue and groove plane (coming and going) 15" lg x 2" w. 7/8" tongue and groove. Two wood open totes with two irons with matching wedges. Plane stamped "P. BROOKS" on one end and "patent" on the other.

Lewis Metallic Beading Plane

Inventor: James A. Lewis

Origin: Detroit, Michigan

Patent Number & Date:
211,516; January 21, 1879.

Metallic bronze plane, triangular shape.
Sides 8 1/2" lg x 2 1/2" w. Two removeable
inserts with blades. Central handle with
two locking keys at the nose. Beading tool
for curved surfaces. One side cuts left,
the other cuts right.

Spotlight Plane

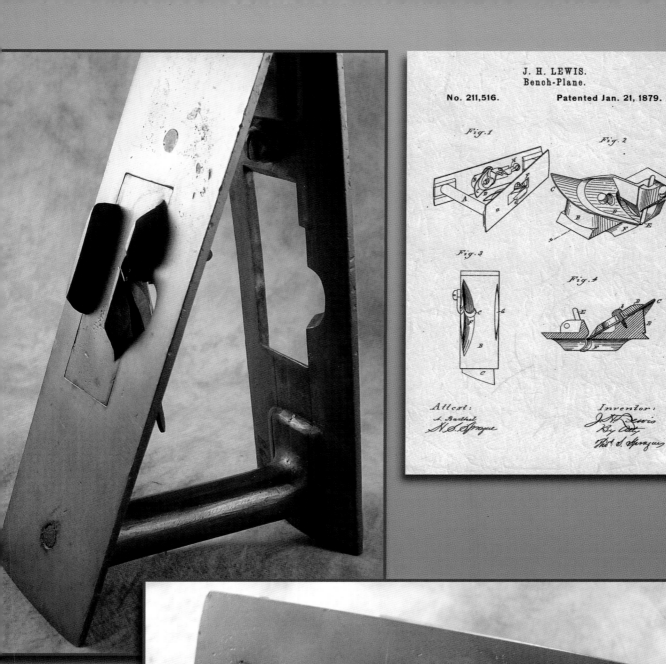

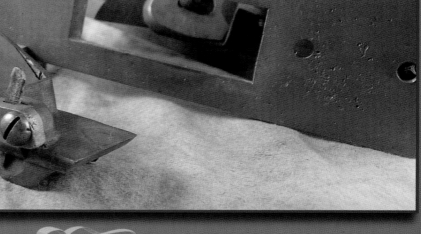

J. H. LEWIS.
Bench-Plane.

No. 211,516.   Patented Jan. 21, 1879.

Fig.1

Fig.2

Fig.3

Fig.4

Attest:

Inventor:

Bailey Tool Patent Planes

Inventor: Bailey Tool Company (Wilson Eckert)

Origin: Woonsocket, Rhode Island

Patent Number & Date:
Defiance Patent #64,001; April 23, 1867.

(above) Iron smooth No. 10 Bailey Tool Company
8 3/4" lg x 2 3/4" w. Double iron 2" w, marked "BAILEY
TOOL CO." Brass nut adjustment feature. Special compound
iron and cap. "DEFIANCE" & "PAT'D APR 23, 1867" on cap.
"BAILEY TOOL CO" in large letters cast into lever cap.

(left) Bailey Tool Company Defiance smooth plane. Plane
has lever type adjustment feature. "BAILEY TOOL CO."
cast into the lever cap. Special compound iron and lever cap.
Beech wood handle and knob.

Inventor: Bailey Tool Company

Origin: Woonsocket, Rhode Island

Patent Number & Date:
No Known Patent.

(left) Bailey Tool Company's "Defiance" jack plane No. 5 size. 12 3/4" lg x 2 3/8" w. Open tote. Non-adjustable.

(below) Bailey Tool Company "Defiance" fore plane No. 7 size. 20 3/4" lg x 2 5/8" w. Open tote. Adjustable brass nut.

Both have double iron marked "BAILEY TOOL CO. WOONSOCKET" with "Battleaxe" logo, and "BAILEY TOOL CO" in large letters cast into lever cap.

Bailey Tool Patent Planes *Continued*

Inventor: J. R. Bailey

Origin: Woonsocket, Rhode Island

Patent Number & Date: 112,675; March 14, 1871.

Iron jointer plane. 21" lg x 3" w. Double iron 2 1/2" w. Beech handle. Brass cap marked "PAT'D July 26, 1870" This patent is for the lever clamp.

Inventor: Joseph R. Bailey

Origin: Woonsocket, Rhode Island

Patent Number & Date: 112,675; March 14, 1871.

(left) Patented iron jack plane 13 1/8" lg x 2 3/8" w. Double iron 2" w. Rosewood handle & knob. Plane has cam lever clamp to secure iron & cap.

(below) Iron smooth plane 8 3/4" lg x 2" w. Double iron 1 1/2" w, stamped "BAILEY TOOL CO. (BATTLEAXE) WOONSOCKET, RI." Rosewood handle and knob. Has cam lever clamp to secure iron and cap.

Bailey Tool
Patent Planes *Continued*

Inventor: Bailey Tool Company

Origin: Woonsocket, Rhode Island

Patent Number & Date: 166,240; August 3, 1875.

Patented iron smooth plane, 8 7/8" lg x 2" w.
Double iron 1 3/4" w, stamped "BAILEY TOOL CO,
WOONSOCKET R,I." "PATENTED AUG 3, 1875"
stamped on brass adjustment nut. Circa 1880.
Cutter adjustment feature, David F. Williams patent.

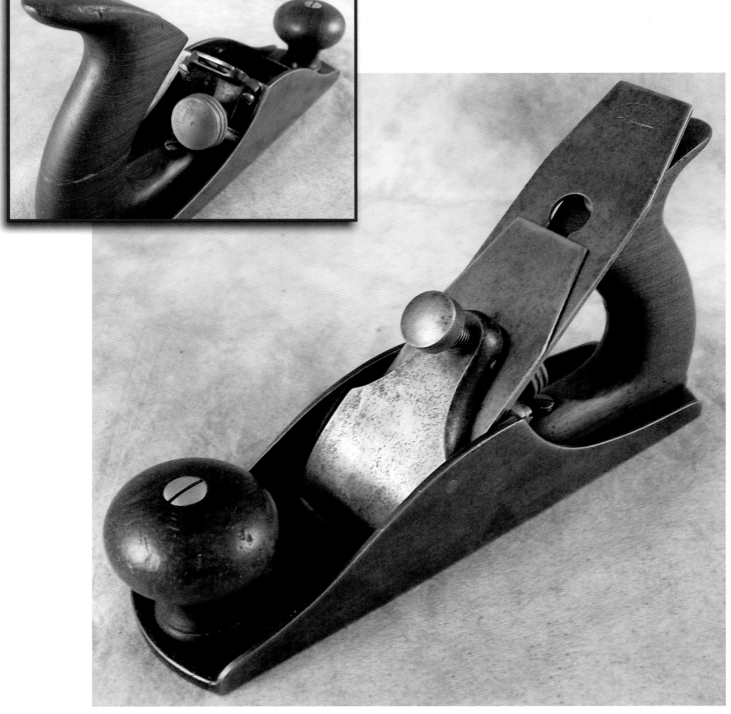

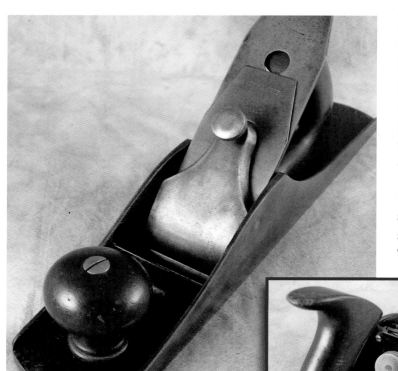

Inventor: Bailey Tool Company

Origin: Woonsocket, Rhode Island

Patent Number & Date: 166,240 (assigned to Bailey Tool Company); August 3, 1875.

(left) David F. Williams patent iron jack plane. Double iron 2" w, marked "BAILEY TOOL CO. WOONSOCKET, R.I." Rosewood handle and knob. "Patented Aug 3, 1875" on brass adjustment nut.

(below) David Williams patent iron fore plane. Iron stamped "DEFIANCE". Offset brass blade adjustment stamped "PATENTED AUG 3, 1875". Iron marked "BAILEY TOOL CO." with "battleaxe" logo.

Bailey Tool Patent Planes *Continued*

Inventor: Bailey Tool Company

Origin: Woonsocket, Rhode Island

Patent Number & Date: Unknown.

(left & below) Bailey Tool Company iron block plane, 6 1/2" lg x 1 15/16" w. Single iron cutter 1 3/8" w. Adjustable. Number designation unknown.

(bottom) Bailey Tool Company block plane 6 3/8" lg. x 1 7/8" w. Adjustable throat. Lateral adjustment. Blade marked "BAILEY TOOL CO. WOONSOCKET, RI" with "battleaxe" logo.

Inventor: Bailey Tool Company

Origin: Woonsocket, Rhode Island

Patent Number & Date: None Known.

Defiance iron block plane 7 5/8" lg x 1 7/8" w.
Single iron 1 5/8" w. No marks. Adjustable
mouth and cutter. Brass knob.

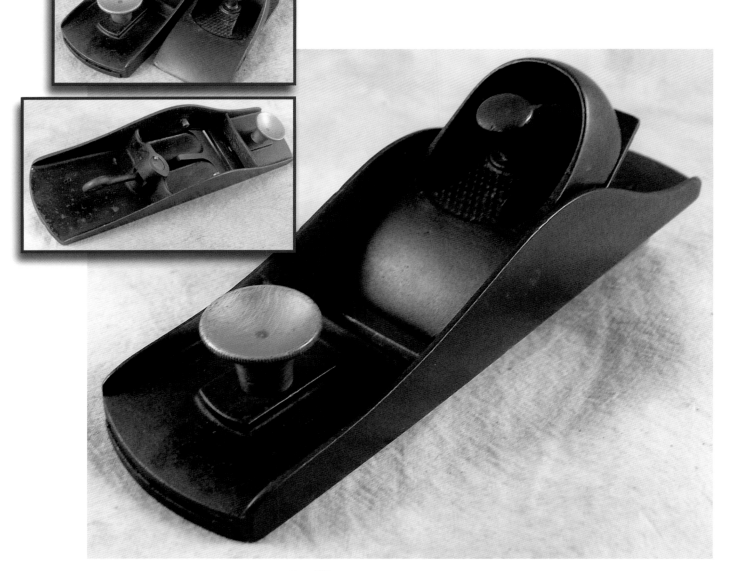

Bailey Tool Patent Planes *Continued*

Inventor: Bailey Tool Company
Origin: Woonsocket, Rhode Island
Patent Number & Date: None Known.
Block plane 7 7/16" lg x 1 7/8" w.
Single iron. Corrugations on bottom
form "BAILEY TOOL COMP".

Inventor: Bailey Tool Company

Origin: Woonsocket, Rhode, Island

Patent Number & Date: None Known.

Rare Bailey Tool Company small block plane 6 3/8" long.
Iron marked "Bailey Tool Co. Woonsocket, R.I"
The plane has the captive cap with a curved lever locking
cam below the blade.

Marples Smooth Plane

Inventor: William Marples

Origin: England

Patent Number & Date: Circa 1891.

William Marples English copy of a Bailey Tool Company's plane. 8 1/4" lg. x 2 1/4" w. Double iron 1 7/8" w (No. 3 size plane). Has unique shape to side rails used on Bailey Tool Company's "Defiance Battleaxe" planes. Floral design on lever cap was influenced by the Bailey Tool Company design.

Scott Miter Plane

Inventor: W. C. Scott

Origin: Cincinnati, Ohio

Patent Number & Date: Circa 1886.

Low angle miter plane manufactured by Scott of Cincinnati, Ohio circa 1886. An advertisement in the publication "Carpenter & Building" shows an ad for the Scott plane. It is advertised as a "Bronze Miter Plane" with fruitwood infill.

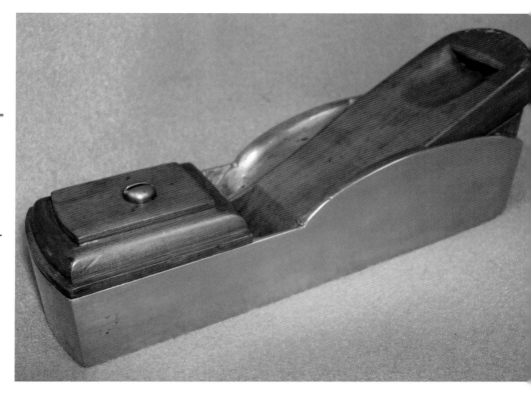

Ohio Tool Smooth Plane

Inventor: Ohio Tool Company

Origin: Columbus, Ohio

Patent Number & Date: 46,166; October 13, 1891.

Wood bottom smooth plane 9 1/2" lg. Double iron 2" w. Blade stamped "OHIO TOOL CO." Toe stamped "OHIO TOOL CO. 304". Michael J. Dunn & William H. Montgomery, Columbus Ohio. Assigned to Ohio Tool Co.

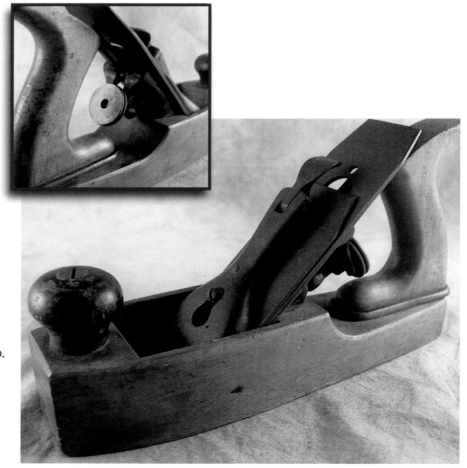

Victor
Patent Planes

Inventor: Leonard Bailey

Origin: Hartford, Connecticut

Patent Number & Date: 185,280; December 12, 1876.

Iron smooth plane, "VICTOR", 9" lg x 2" w.
Double iron 1 3/4" w. Cap iron stamped "L. BAILEY,
PATENT APRIL 23, 1867 - DEC 12, 1876."
This model has a pin on the frog lever that engages
one in a series of 1/8" diameter holes in the iron.

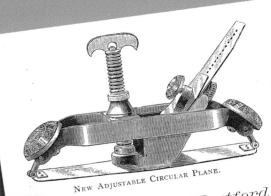

LEONARD BAILEY & CO.,

MANUFACTURERS OF

LEONARD BAILEY'S

PATENT VICTOR PLANES,

TRY SQUARES, BEVELS,

Spoke Shaves, Box Scrapers, &c.

NEW ADJUSTABLE CIRCULAR PLANE.

Hartford, Conn., Jan. 22nd 1881

J. E. Blood,

Dear Sir,

Your letter of 20th at hand. Will say in reply. I do not think it best for me to undertake to make the hatchets. from the fact that I have not been able to procure the right class of help to do the work, on our own goods. which I want to do. We are way behind on _____ ____ ____ds on our list now and untill ____ ____ way to supply our regular goods, ____ ____t be good policy to go into anything ____ ____ Bailey has asked the same thing ____ ____ him the same answer. Would like ____ S. A. B. at any time when convenient

Yours truly,

L. Bailey.

Leonard Bailey *1825-1905*

Victor
Patent Planes *Continued*

Inventor: Leonard Bailey

Origin: Hartford, Connecticut

Patent Number & Date: 185,280; December 12, 1876.

Iron jointer (below), "VICTOR", 22 1/2" lg x 2 3/4" w. Double iron 2 1/4" w. Victor plane knob, metal handle, eccentric lever device (blade is a replacement).

Iron fore plane (right), 18" lg x 2 3/4" w. Double iron 2 3/8" w. Cap iron stamped "L BAILEY, PAT. APRIL 23, 1867 - DEC 12, 1876." Eccentric lever device. Cap iron incorporates a lever device patent #285,546; September 25, 1883.

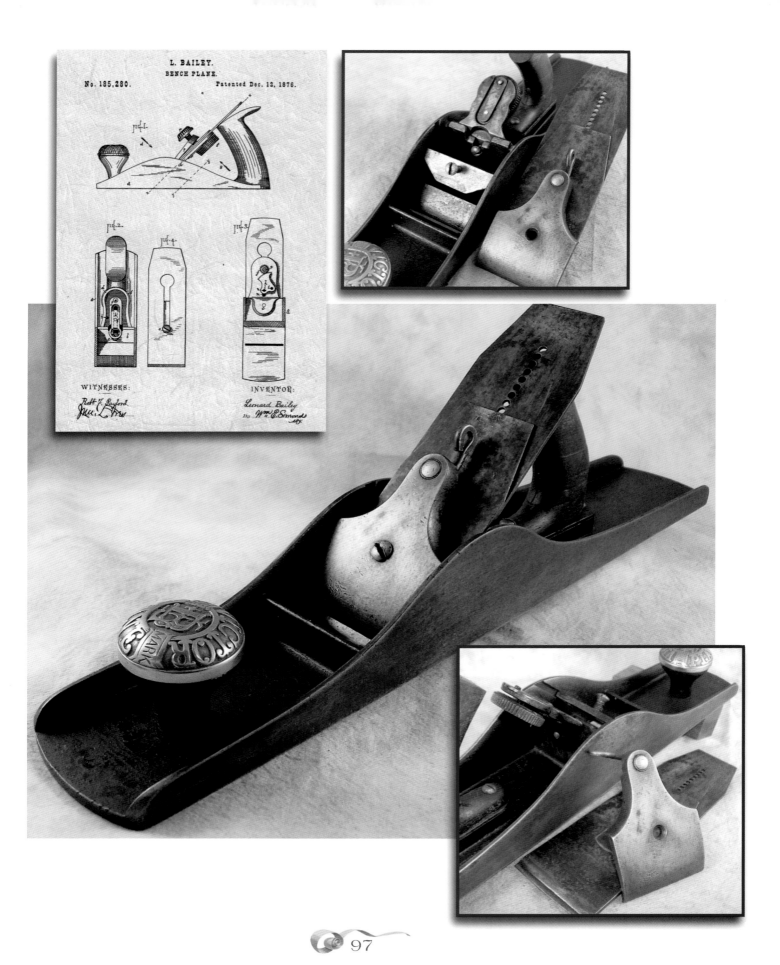

Victor
Patent Planes *Continued*

Inventor: Leonard Bailey

Origin: Hartford, Connecticut

Patent Number & Date: 185,280; December 12, 1876.

Bailey "Victor" No.1 iron block plane (below), 6 1/4 " lg x 1 15/16" w. Iron 1 1/2" w. stamped "L. BAILEY PATENT DEC 12, 1876." Adjustable mouth and cutter.

L. Bailey's "VICTOR" No. 2 iron block plane (right), 7" lg x 2" w. Single iron 1 3/4" w, stamped "L.BAILEY'S PATENT DEC. 12, 1876". Eccentric lever device.

Victor
Patent Planes *Continued*

Inventor: Leonard Bailey

Origin: Hartford, Connecticut

Patent Number & Date: 185,280; December 12, 1876.

Bailey Victor No. 2 1/4. 7 1/2" lg x 1 3/4" w.
Adjustable throat. Iron removable rear handle.
Metal front knob. Eccentric lever device patented by
L.Bailey, #285,546; September 25, 1883.

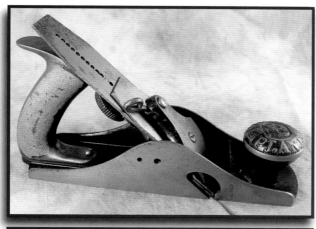

Inventor: Leonard Bailey

Origin: Hartford, Connecticut

Patent Number & Date:
189,415; April 10, 1877 & 285,546; September 25,1883.

L. Bailey's Victor Smooth Rabbet & Filletster
Plane No. 11 1/2. 8 7/8" lg x 2 5/16" w.
Double iron 2 5/16" w. Fence missing.

Victor Patent Planes *Continued*

Inventor: Leonard Bailey

Origin: Hartford, Connecticut

Patent Number & Date: 165,356; July 6, 1875.

L. Bailey's Victor No. 14 Combination plane.
9 3/4" lg x 3" w, including arms. Single iron and spur
cutter, each 3/8" w. Nickel plated handle and knob.
Patent issued to Charles Miller & Leonard Bailey,
New Britain, Connecticut. Assigned to Leonard Bailey.

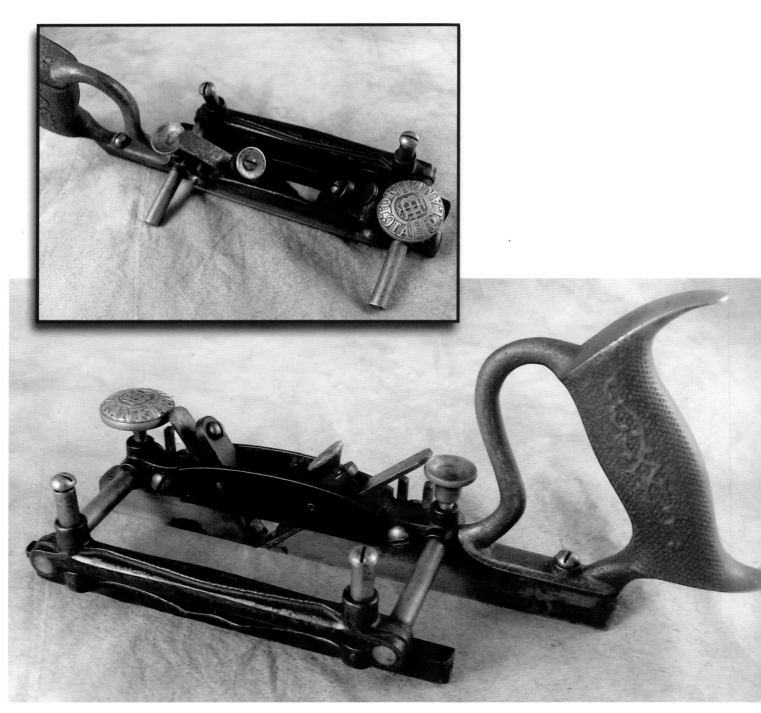

Inventor: Leonard Bailey

Origin: Hartford, Connecticut

Patent Number & Date: 196,068; October 16, 1877.

(top) Bailey's "LITTLE VICTOR" 50 toy size adjustable block plane. Single iron 1" w. Plane has full adjustment with knurled brass nut to secure iron. Cog wheel has nib that engages slots under the iron for adjustment. 3 1/16" lg x 1 1/4" w.

(bottom) Bailey's "LITTLE VICTOR" toy size iron block plane No. 51. 3 3/16" lg. x 1 1/4" w. Single iron 1" w, not marked. Non-adjustable. Plane has "cog" wheel screw to secure the iron.

Victor
Patent Planes *Continued*

Inventor: Leonard Bailey

Origin: Hartford, Connecticut

Patent Number & Date: Circa 1880.

L. Bailey's Victor No. 12 pocket block plane.
4 1/2" lg. x 1 1/2" w. Iron 1 1/4" w. Metal front knob.
Rear metal adjusting knob with
"L B. VICTOR PLANE TRADE MARK".

Katz Smooth Plane

Inventor: Julius Katz

Origin: Cincinnati, Ohio

Patent Number & Date:
102,406; April 26,1870.

Patented smooth plane. Maple body with lignum vitae sole dovetailed to plane bottom forward of the cutter. Bottom adjustment is for opening and closing the mouth of the plane. 6 1/4" lg x 2 1/16" w. Toe stamped "PAT'D APRIL 28th '70 J KATZ".

Brice Jack Plane

Inventor: John Brice

Origin: Sandy Hill, New York

Patent Number & Date:
337,454; February 8, 1887.

Beech jack plane 16" lg x 2 7/8" w. Double iron. "BROWN TOOL CO." stamped on toe. Patent date on metal adjustment wheel. Iron 2 1/4" w, marked "AUBURN TOOL CO. THISTLE BRAND AUBURN NY".

Duval Dado Planes

Inventor: Theodore Duval

Origin: Hartford, Connecticut

Patent Number & Date: Patent applied for.

Duval's adjustable dado plane. Two plane halves that are adjusted by turning screws for a desired width. Heel stamped "PATENT APPLIED FOR". Most likely this is Duval's first concept for an adjustable dado plane prior to receiving patent #97,177; November 12, 1869.

Inventor: Theodore Duval

Origin: Hartford, Connecticut

Patent Number & Date:
97,177; November 23, 1869.

Adjustable dado plane 9 1/2" lg x 1 3/8" w.
Twin irons and wedges set side by side.
Brass adjustment screws and depth stop.
"Hartford Plane Co" stamped on toe.
"1337" stamped on heel.

Worrall Patent Planes

Inventor: Thomas D. Worrall

Origin: Lowell, Massachusetts

Patent Number & Date: 16,309; December 23, 1856.

Wood jointer plane 28" lg x 3 3/8" w. Double iron stamped "MULTIFORM MOULDING PLANE CO - BOSTON". Iron cap. Bolt through heel locks cutter and ratchet mechanism for the cutter. Toe stamped "COPELAND & CO. WARRANTED".

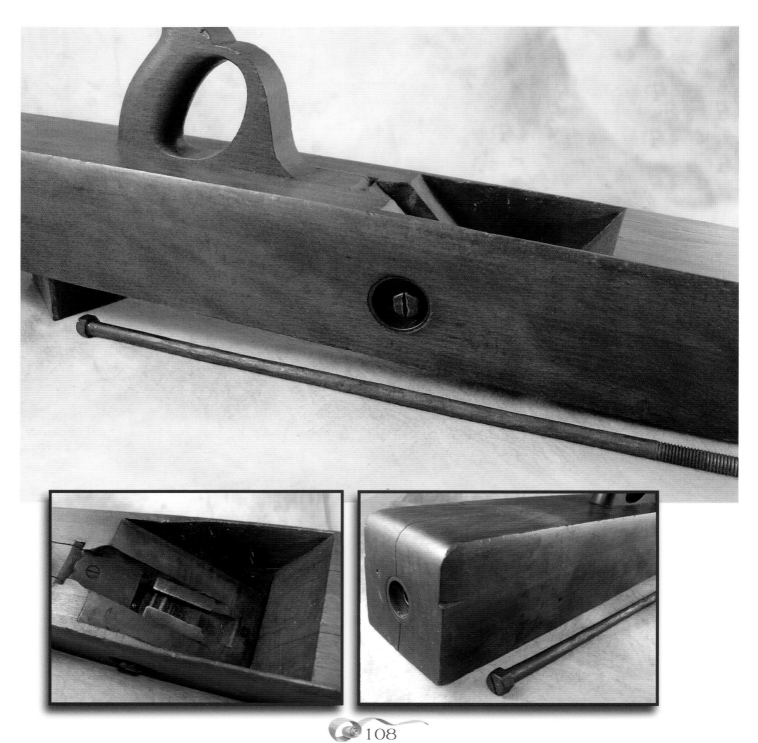

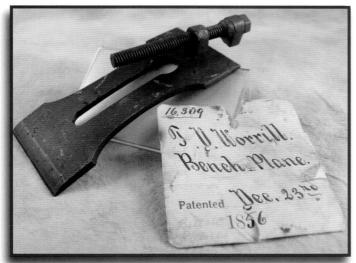

Inventor: Thomas D. Worrall

Origin: Lowell, Massachusetts

Patent Number & Date: 16,309; December 23, 1856.

Worrall's Patent wood jointer plane,
21" lg x 3" w. Iron 2 3/8" w.

"COPELAND & CO. WARRANTED"
stamped on toe. Cutter adjustment and curved cap iron
shown in patent #16,309; December 23, 1856.

WORRALL'S PATENT PLANES,

MANUFACTURED AND FOR SALE BY

COPELAND & CO., HUNTINGTON, MASS.,

AND AT THE GENERAL DEPOT,

41 BRATTLE ST., (under the Quincy House,)...BOSTON.

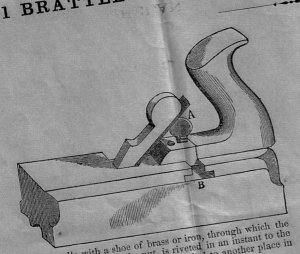

A handle with a shoe of brass or iron, through which the thumbscrew works in the nut, is riveted in an instant to the plane by a turn of the screw, and shifted to another place in as short a time.

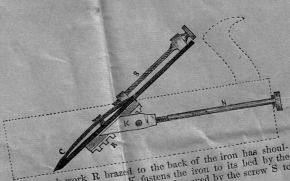

The rack work R brazed to the back of the iron has shoulders, by which the clamp K fastens the iron to its bed by the shaft N. The cap C is curved, and moved by the screw S to any point, with the utmost nicety.

You are respectfully informed that the "Multiform Moulding Plane Company" have established a Depot at 41 Brattle Street, Boston, for the sale of "Worrall's Patent Moulding, Bench and Ship Planes."

The advantages these Planes have over the old kind are so many and various that we cannot enumerate them in a circular, but solicit your personal inspection, feeling confident that their superiority will be evident.

The highest premium has been awarded to the exhibitors of these Planes by the Mass. Mechanics' Association, American Institute, New York, and awards from all other States where they have been on exhibition. This, together with the unqualified approbation received from all practical carpenters who have used them, prove their great superiority over the old Plane.

Orders from the country, accompanied by satisfactory city reference, promptly attended to.

Price Lists furnished on application.

J. B. CALDICOTT, AGENT.

GEO. T. SHIPLEY, SECRETARY.

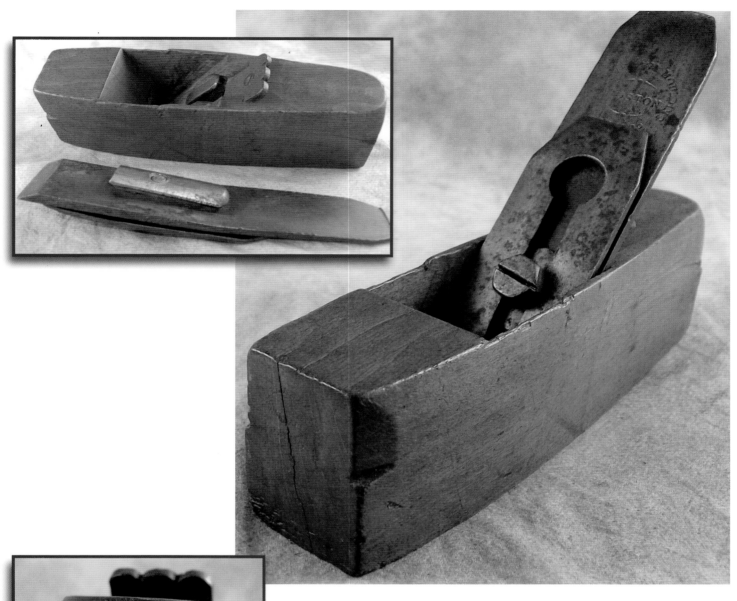

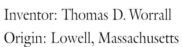

Inventor: Thomas D. Worrall

Origin: Lowell, Massachusetts

Patent Number & Date: 17,657; June 23, 1857.

Worrall's Patent wood block plane 7 1/2" lg x 2" w.
Single iron 1 7/8" w, stamped "MULTIFORM
MOULDING PLANE CO. BOSTON."
"LOWELL PLANE & TOOL CO." stamped on toe.

Worrall Patent Planes *Continued*

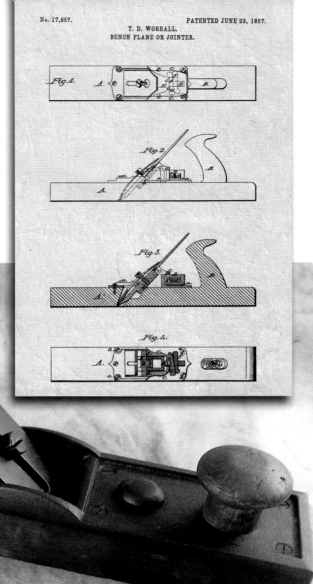

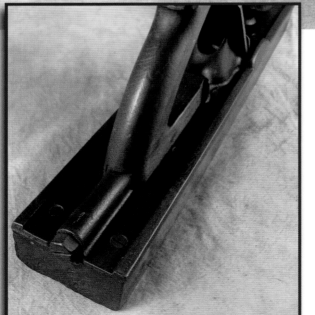

Inventor: Thomas D. Worrall

Origin: Lowell, Massachusetts

Patent Number & Date: 17,657; June 23, 1857.

Worrall's patent wood bottom jack plane.
Full iron top plate 15 13/16" lg x 2 5/8" w.
Double iron 2" w, marked
"MULTIFORM MOULDING PLANE CO.,
BOSTON." Toe stamped "PAT MAY 27, 1856."
Wooden tote, knob and strike button.
Longitudinal cutter adjustment feature.

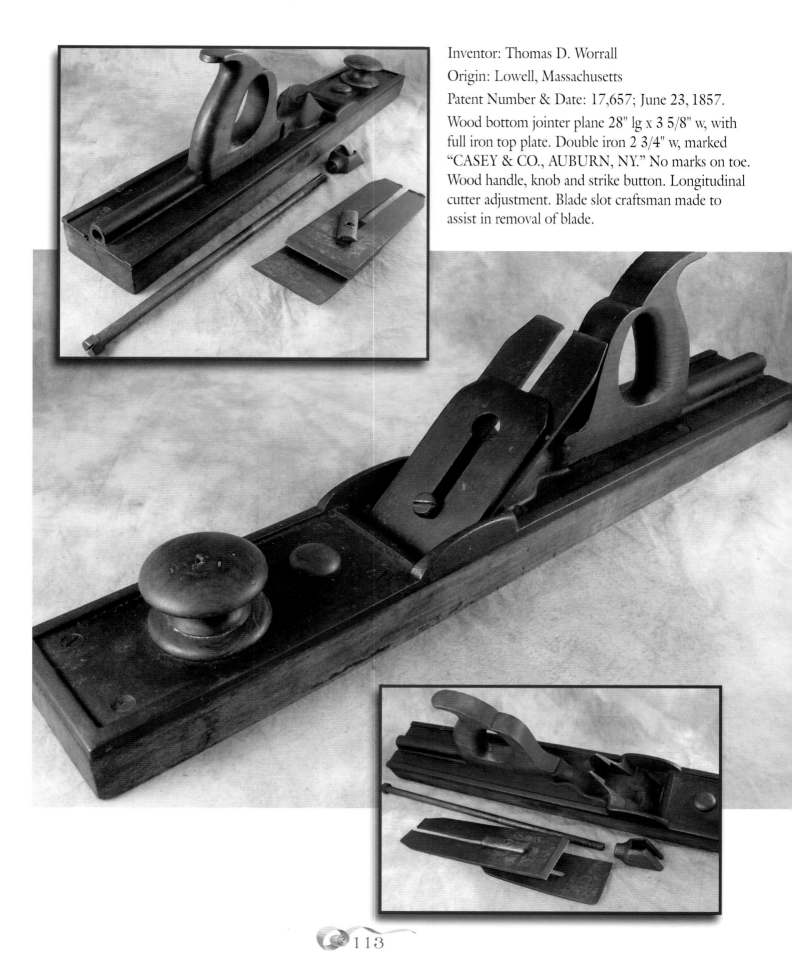

Inventor: Thomas D. Worrall

Origin: Lowell, Massachusetts

Patent Number & Date: 17,657; June 23, 1857.

Wood bottom jointer plane 28" lg x 3 5/8" w, with full iron top plate. Double iron 2 3/4" w, marked "CASEY & CO., AUBURN, NY." No marks on toe. Wood handle, knob and strike button. Longitudinal cutter adjustment. Blade slot craftsman made to assist in removal of blade.

Worrall
Patent Planes *Continued*

Inventor: Thomas D. Worrall

Origin: Lowell, Massachusetts

Patent Number & Date: 17,657; June 23, 1857.

Worral's Patent Wood Bottom Fore Plane.
22" lg x 3 1/4" w. Double iron 2 1/2" w, stamped
"MULTIFORM MOULDING PLANE CO."
Toe stamped "WORRALL PAT. MAY 27, 1856-
JUNE 23, 1857, LOWELL, MASS."
Patent date cast in large letters in iron top.

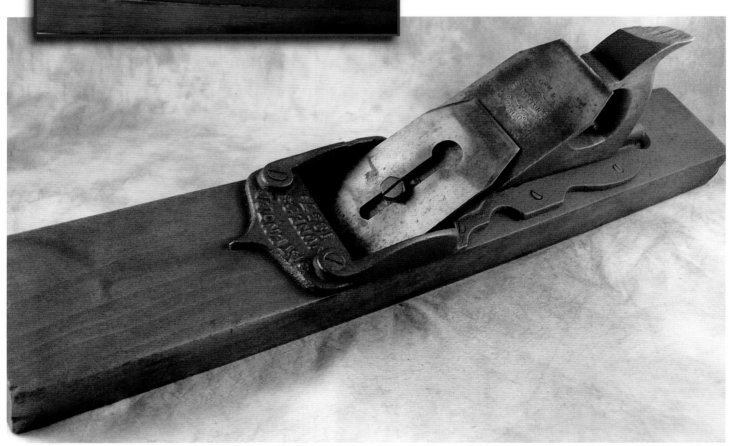

Inventor: Thomas D. Worrall

Origin: Lowell, Massachusetts

Patent Number & Date: 17,657; June 23, 1857.

Worrall's Patent wood bottom open tote smooth plane (right), 8 1/2" lg x 2 1/2" w. Double iron 2" w. Longitudinal blade attachment feature. No front knob. "MULTIFORM MOULDING PLANE CO" stamped on iron. "LOWELL PLANE & TOOL CO, MAY 27, 1856 & JUNE 1857" stamped on toe.

Wood bottom jack plane (below), 16" lg x 2 3/4" w. Double iron 2" w, stamped "MULTIFORM MOULDING PLANE CO. BOSTON." Toe stamped "LOWELL PLANE CO. WORRALL'S PATENT MAY 27, 1856" Iron top plate. Open tote, no front knob. Longitudinal cutter adjustment feature.

Worrall
Patent Planes *Continued*

Inventor: Thomas D. Worrall

Origin: Lowell, Massachusetts

Patent Number & Date: 17,657; June 23, 1857.

Worrall's Patent handled wood bottom smooth plane 9" lg x 2 3/4" w. Double iron 2" w, marked "CASEY & CO., AUBURN, NY." Longitudinal cutter adjustment feature. Plane stamped "LOWELL PLANE & TOOL CO., WORRALL'S PATENT MAY 27, 1856."

Mander Chamfer Plane

Inventor: James A. Mander

Origin: Phildelphia, Pennsylvania

Patent Number & Date:
314,338; March 2, 1885.

Chamfer plane, beech stock 7" lg x 2" w.
Single iron 1 1/2" w. Mander was a British
citizen and apparently brought this idea
from England with him. Mander patent
1/3 assigned to Maurice Dillin.

Robinson Bench Plane

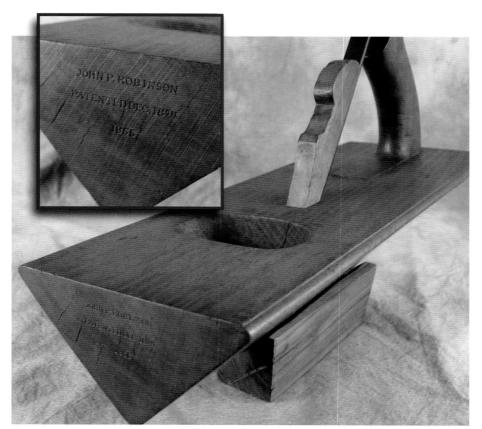

Inventor: John P. Robinson

Origin: Matteawan, New York

Patent Number & Date:
13,957; December 18, 1853.

Wooden core box plane 12 3/8" lg
x 4 3/8" w. Iron 7/16" w. Maple body
with cherry handle and wedge.
Patent date on toe.

Phillips Presentation Plough Plane

Inventor: Philips Plough Plane Company

Origin: Boston, Massachusetts

Patent Number & Date: 67,671; August 13, 1867.

Phillip's presentation plough plane. Bronze frame. Rosewood handle and fence trim. "THE PHILLIP'S PLOUGH PLANE CO. - BOSTON, MASS TRADE B & R MARK" engraved in Old English on right side of skate. "CAST BY THE METALLIC COMPRESSION CASTING CO. - NO. 46 CONGRESS ST. BOSTON". engraved on left side of skate.

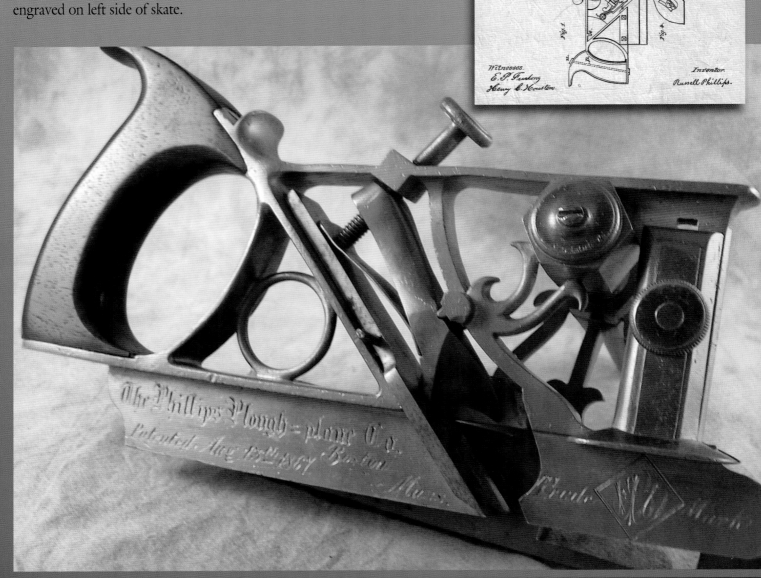

The Phillips Plough-plane Co
Patented Aug 13th 1867 Boston

Spotlight Plane

Taber Patent Planes

Inventor: Taber Experimental Model

Origin: New Bedford, Massachusetts

Patent Number & Date: None Known.

Beech wood jack plane (below), 16" lg x 3 1/8" w. Double iron 2 1/4" w, stamped "PROVIDENCE TOOL CO. WARRANTED." No lever cap. Frog screw is T-shaped and when rotated will secure the cutter and cap iron. "W. H. TAYLOR" stamped 3 times on toe. Possibly a prototype.

Beech smooth plane (right), 10" lg including handle overhang x 3 7/16" w. Double iron 2 5/8" w, stamped "PROVIDENCE TOOL CO. WARRANTED. W. H. TAYLOR". "W.H." stamped twice on toe.

Taber
Patent Planes *Continued*

Inventor: Wing H. Taber

Origin: Lowell, Massachusetts

Patent Number & Date: None Known.

Beech wood rounding plane 7" lg x 2 3/8" w.
Double iron 1 3/4" w, unmarked.
Equipped with Taber's earliest type cap and screw.
"W. H. TABER" stamped once on toe,
"LOWELL" stamped twice on toe.

Inventor: Taber & Abbott

Origin: Lowell, Massachusetts

Patent Number & Date:
46,614; February 28, 1865.

Wood smooth plane 8" lg x 2 3/8" w.
Toe stamped "TABOR & ABBOTT
PAT'D FEB 28, 1865".
Iron stamped "WELDON".
Blade locking device possibly an
experimental design.

Inventor: Wing H. Taber

Origin: New Bedford, Massachusetts

Patent Number & Date: 46,614; February 28, 1865.

Beech smooth plane 9" lg x 2 5/16" w. Single iron
1 13/16" w, stamped "SWINSCOW & MANUEL."
Metal rod connects plane side walls. Wedge lock
lever cap secures the cutter. "W H TABER"
stamped once vertically and once horizontally
forming a letter "T".

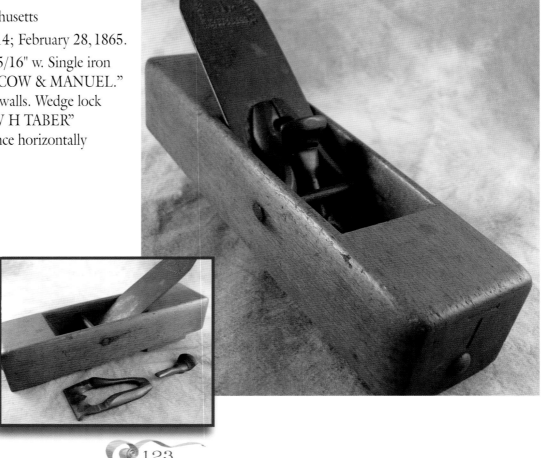

Taber
Patent Planes *Continued*

Inventor: Wing H. Taber

Origin: New Bedford, Massachusetts

Patent Number & Date:
46,614; February 28, 1865.

Beech block plane 8" lg x 2 11/16" w. Double Iron 2" w, marked "MOULSON BROTHERS". Wing H. Taber - Lowell, Massachusetts patent #46,614; February 28, 1865 assigned to himself and Thomas H. Abbot.

Inventor: Wing H. Taber

Origin: New Bedford, Massachusetts

Patent Number & Date:
46,614; February 28, 1865.

Beech wood smooth plane (right),
8 1/2" lg x 2 9/16" w. Double iron 2" w,
marked "BUTCHER". Toe stamped
"TABER PLANE CO. NEW BEDFORD.
MASS. PAT'D FEB 28-65."

Beech wood fore plane (below),
19" lg x 2 11/16" w. Double iron 2 1/4" w,
marked "JARVIS & LINTON". Toe stamped
"TABER PLANE CO. NEW BEDFORD,
MASS. PATENTED FEB. 28, 1865".

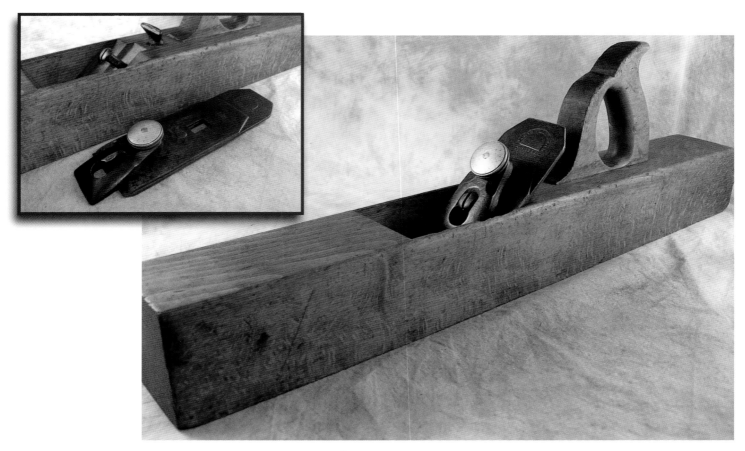

Taber
Patent Planes *Continued*

Inventor: Taber Plane

Origin: New Bedford, Massachusetts

Patent Number & Date: 46,614; February 28, 1865.

Beech wood smooth plane 8" lg x 2 1/2" w. Double iron 2" w, stamped "W. BUTCHER-WARRANTED." Unique "door knob" type hollowed cast iron cap screw with a decorated 1 15/16" diameter brass facing soldered to the top. "TABER & ABBOTT PAT'D FEB. 28, 1865" stamped on toe.

Tolman
Patent Planes

Inventor: Thomas J. Tolman

Origin: South Scituate, Massachusetts

Patent Number & Date: 164,112; January 13, 1857.

Rabbet rosewood plane, unmarked. 11 1/8" lg x 1 1/16" w. Double iron 1" w, marked "I.S.W." Adjustable mouth mechanism. Front of plane is moveable by means of a screw attachment. A possible Tolman patent.

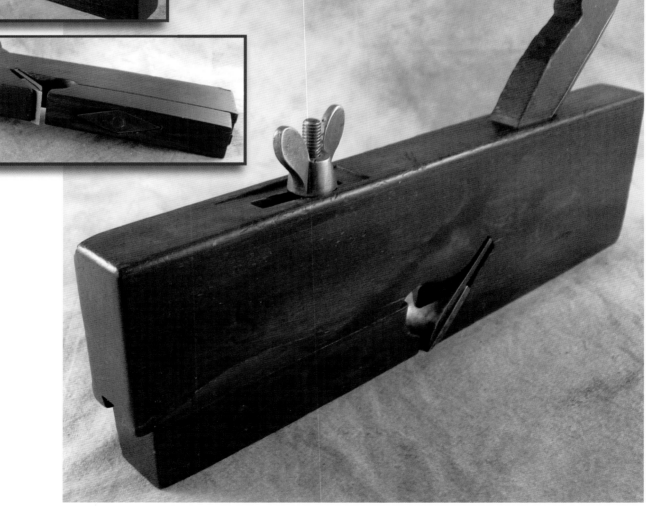

Jacobsen Jointer Plane

Inventor: Clark J. Jacobsen

Origin: Brooklyn, New York

Patent Number & Date:
420,396; January 28, 1890.

Patented iron jointer plane. Closed tote, curved nose and heel. Small front knob 1 1/2" diameter. Double iron marked "SARGENT & CO. NEW HAVEN, CONN." A metal plate is mounted to the wall in front of throat which attaches to a long threaded bolt that enters the toe of the plane. This mechanism adjusts the throat opening.

Arnold Jack Plane

Inventor: William F. Arnold

Origin: Oakland, California

Patent Number & Date:
840,418; January 1, 1907.

Wood bottom jack plane 16 1/8" x 2 3/16" w. Iron unmarked. "PAT. 1907" cast into frog. Plane has metal insert for bottom wear.

Thompson Fore Plane

Inventor: G. M. Thompson

Origin: Boston, Massachusetts

Patent Number & Date: 153,399; July 21, 1874.

Iron fore plane. Blade marked "G.M. THOMPSON PATENT JULY 21, 1874". Corrugated top and bottom. Cutter adjustment is a lever arm that engages teeth on the back of the blade similar to L. Bailey's patent August 8, 1867. 18 1/2" lg x 2 3/4" w.

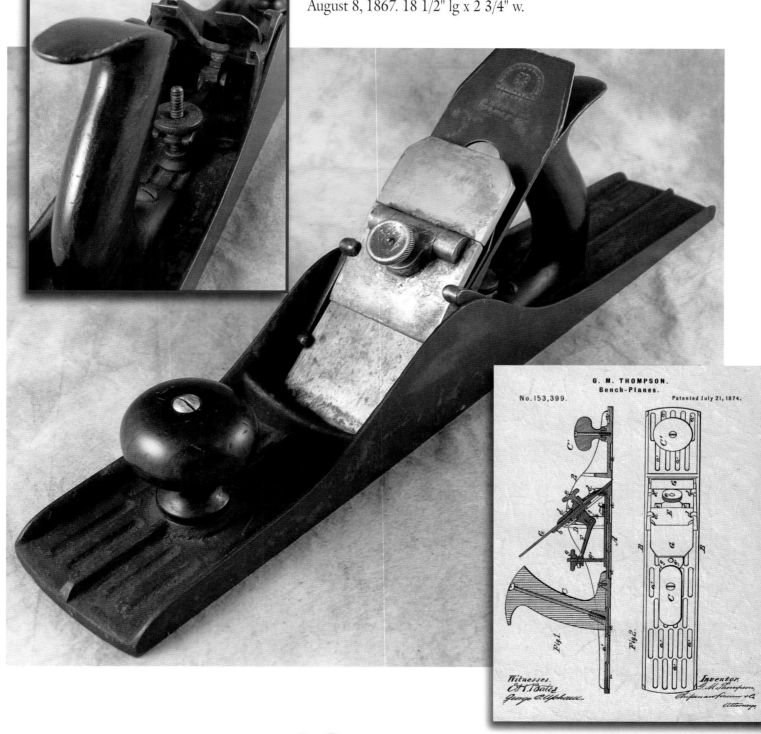

Price
Smooth
Plane

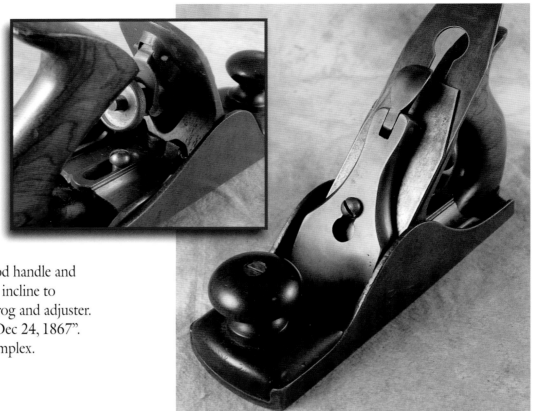

Inventor: Henry B. Price

Origin: New York, New York

Patent Number & Date:
216,986; June 17, 1879.

Iron smooth plane with rosewood handle and
knob. Patent features a stair step incline to
adjust the pitch of the all brass frog and adjuster.
Blade marked "L. Bailey patent Dec 24, 1867".
Patent features are somewhat complex.

Kendall
Jointer Plane

Inventor: H. L. Kendall

Origin: Baltimore, Maryland

Patent Number & Date:
20,493; June 8, 1858.

Wood jointer 22" lg. x 3 5/8" w.
Double iron 3" w, marked
"PROVIDENCE TOOL CO."
Adjustable wood insert in
front of the mouth to adjust
for mouth wear. Toe marked
"H.L. Kendall" in script,
"127 LEXINGTON ST", "Balto"
in script with patent date.

Glover Fore Plane

Inventor: Winslow B. Glover

Origin: Boston, Massachusetts

Patent Number & Date:
108,586; October 25, 1870.

Wood fore plane 22" lg x 3 1/2" w.
Double iron 2 1/2" w.
"H. WELLS WMS-BURG, MASS"
stamped on toe. Iron stamped
"A.L. WHITING & CO.
WORCESTER MASS." (plane logo).
Iron also marked "W.B. GLOVER
PAT APD FOR".

Cole Circular Plane

Inventor: William A. Cole

Origin: New York, New York

Patent Number & Date: 5,620; June 6, 1848.

Beech circular plane 8" lg x 2 1/2" w.
with flexible sole. Iron marked
"BALDWIN TOOL CO. BUTCHERS
CAST STEEL WARRANTED".

Birmingham
Patent Planes

Inventor: Birmingham Plane Company

Origin: Birmingham, Connecticut

Patent Number & Date: 296,207; April 1, 1884.

Iron rabbet plane (this page), 9" lg x 2" w. Single iron 2" w. Non-adjustable. Circular brass cap screw. T-shaped carriagemaker's rabbet. Patented by George D. Mosher and William F. Ford.

Iron rabbet plane (right), 8" lg x 1 3/4" w. Single iron 1 3/4" w. No marks. Non-adjustable square nut cap screw. T shaped carriagemaker's plane. Patented by George D. Mosher and William F. Ford.

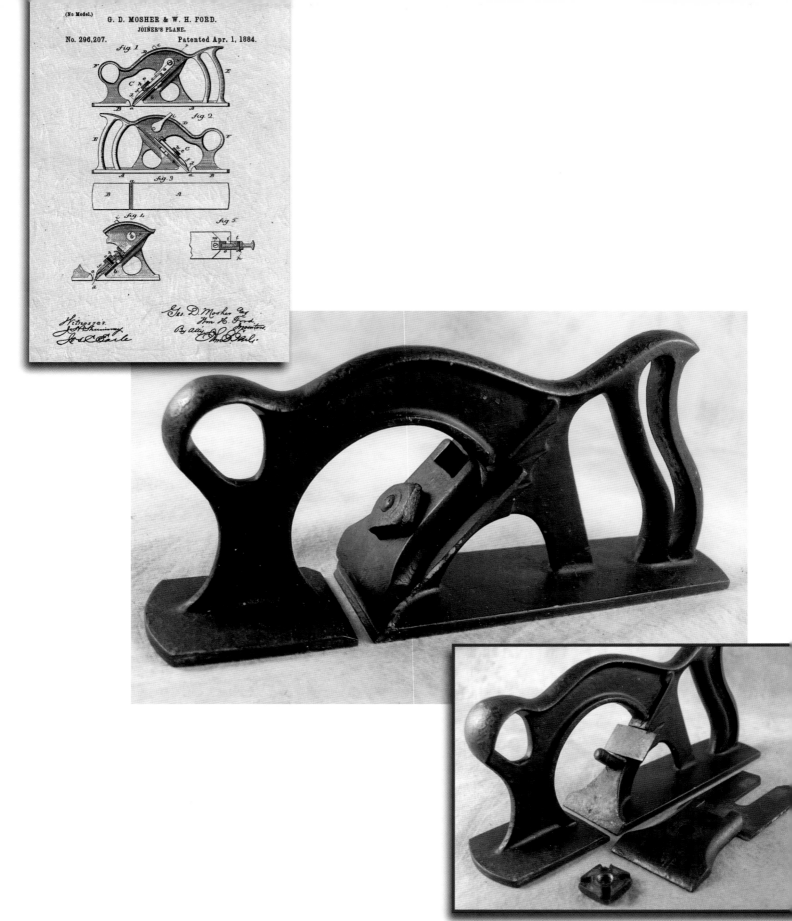

Birmingham Patent Planes *Continued*

Inventor: Birmingham Plane Company

Origin: Birmingham, Connecticut

Patent Number & Date: 296,207; April 1, 1884.

T shaped carriagemaker's iron rabbet plane. Miniature 4" lg. Cutter 1 1/4" w. A very small and rare plane. Birmingham Plane Company. George Mosher and William Ford patent.

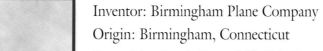

Inventor: Birmingham Plane Company

Origin: Birmingham, Connecticut

Patent Number & Date: 309,400; December 16, 1884.

Wood bottom jack plane. Beech base 15" lg x 2 9/16" w.
Single iron 1 15/16" w, marked "THE BIRMINGHAM PLANE MFG CO."
Plane has same adjustment mechanism as used on cast iron planes.
Patented by George E. Mosher - Birmingham, Connecticut.

Birmingham Patent Planes *Continued*

Inventor: Birmingham Plane Company

Origin: Birmingham, Connecticut

Patent Number & Date:
309,400; December 16, 1884.

Iron jack plane 14" lg x 2 1/2" w. Blade 2" w.
No marks. Clamp plate feature secures blade.
Patented by George D. Mosher.

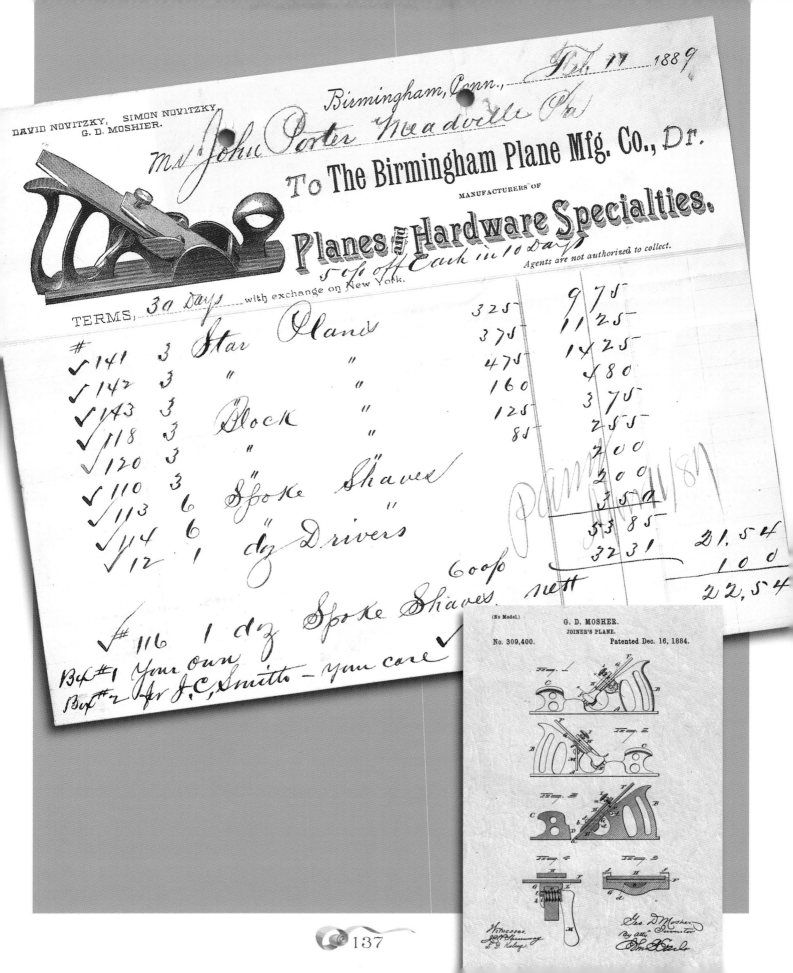

Birmingham Patent Planes *Continued*

Inventor: Derby Plane Company

Origin: Birmingham, Connecticut

Patent Number & Date: 413,329; October, 22, 1889.

Wood bottom smooth B-plane 10" lg x 2 1/2" w.
Double iron 2" w, marked "B PLANE PAT'D OCT 22, 1889."
Wood handle and knob. No. 36.

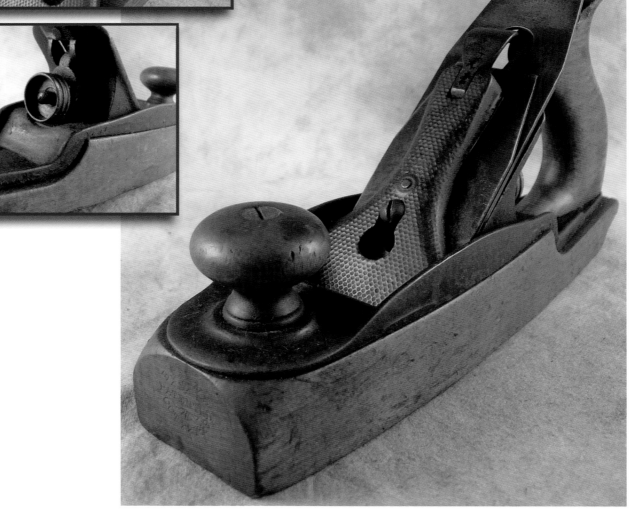

Inventor: Birmingham Plane Company

Origin: Birmingham, Connecticut

Patent Number & Date: 413,329; October 22, 1889.

Wood bottom plane 20" lg x 3" w. Double iron
2 1/8" w, stamped "B - PLANE PAT'D OCT 22,
1889." "BEES" in the imprint stamped on the toe.

Birmingham Patent Planes *Continued*

Inventor: Derby Plane Company

Origin: Birmingham, Connecticut

Patent Number & Date: 413,300; October 22, 1889.

"B" plane made by Birmingham Plane Company.
No. 3 size. Double iron marked "B PLANE PATENTED"
George D. Mosher's patent 413,300. Plane made
only to 1891.

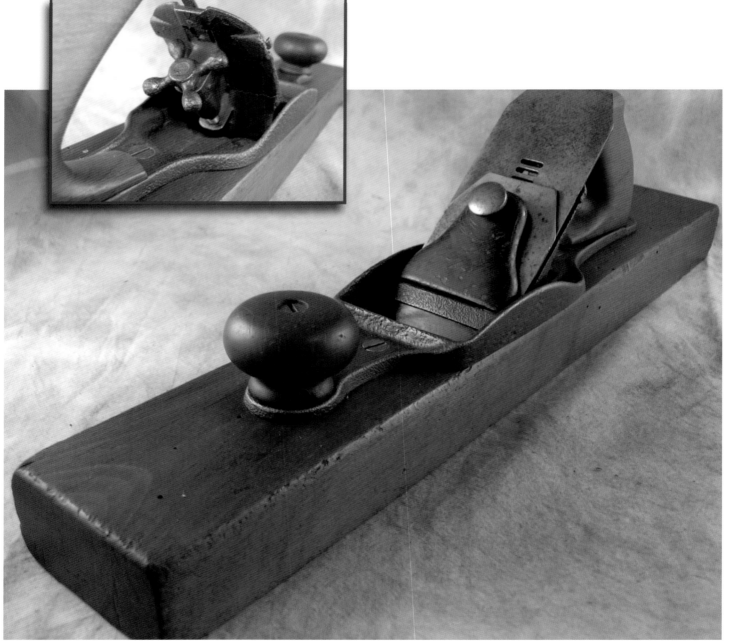

Inventor: Birmingham Plane Company

Origin: Birmingham, Connecticut

Patent Number & Date: 508,386; November 7, 1893.

Wood bottom fore plane 20" lg x 3" w. Double iron 2 1/2" w, marked "THE BIRMINGHAM PLANE MANUFACTURING CO." Patented by Oliver R. Hayworth, Tarkio, Missouri. One half of patent assigned to Amon Curfman of Tarkio, Missouri.

Birmingham Patent Planes *Continued*

Inventor: Birmingham Plane Company

Origin: Birmingham, Connecticut

Patent Number & Date: October 22, 1889.

Unmarked Birmingham Plane Company toy block plane. 3 1/4" lg x 1 1/4" w. No lateral adjustment feature.

Inventor: Birmingham Plane Company

Origin: Birmingham, Connecticut

Patent Number & Date: None Known

Toy sized iron block plane 3 1/4" lg x 1 1/4" w. Iron 1" w. Remains of "BIRMINGHAM PLANE CO" stamped on iron.

Lateral adjustment lever

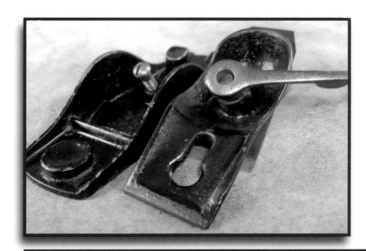

Inventor: Birmingham Plane Company

Origin: Birmingham, Connecticut

Patent Number & Date: Unknown

Birmingham Plane Company iron block plane.
No. 108, 5 1/2" lg x 1 1/4" w.
Screw through cap locks blade.

Birmingham
Patent Planes *Continued*

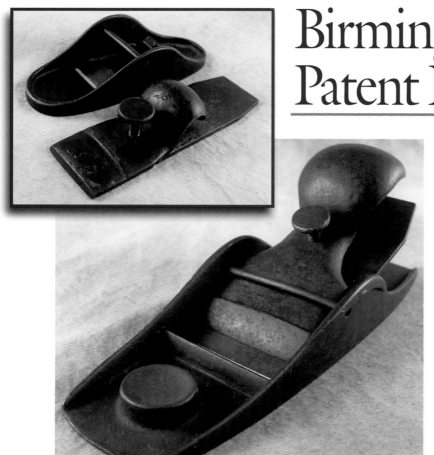

Inventor: Birmingham Plane Company

Origin: Birmingham, Connecticut

Patent Number & Date:
413,329; October 22, 1889.

Iron block plane 7" lg x 2" w. Single iron 1 5/8" w, marked "THE BIRMINGHAM PLANE CO." Solon Rust patent for blade grooves on back of blade to assist lever in blade adjusting.

Inventor:
Birmingham Plane Company

Origin:
Birmingham, Connecticut

Patent Number & Date:
Unknown.

Birmingham Plane Company toy block plane, 4" lg x 1" w. Thumb screw blade lock with cap iron and palm rest . "Boat shape" plane body.

Inventor: Birmingham Plane Company

Origin: Birmingham, Connecticut

Patent Number & Date: Circa 1885.

Birmingham Plane Company adjustable metal block plane with brass front knob. Thumb screw secures blade. Plane No. 118.

Hopper Smooth Plane

Inventor: William C. Hopper

Origin: Pittsburgh, Pennsylvania

Patent Number & Date:
12,234; January 16, 1855.

Beech smooth plane 8" lg x
2 11/16" w. Single iron 2" w,
no marks. Iron mouth piece in sole.
Toe stamped "WM. C. HOPPER -
PATENT JAN-16-1855".

Doscher Jack Plane

Inventor: Marten Doscher

Origin: New York, New York

Patent Number & Date:
390,374; October 2, 1888.

Beech wood bottom jack plane
18 7/8" lg x 2 3/4" w. Iron 2 1/4" w,
marked "W. BUTCHER."
"MARTEN DOSCHER–NEW YORK–
PAT. OCT 2, 1888" stamped on toe.

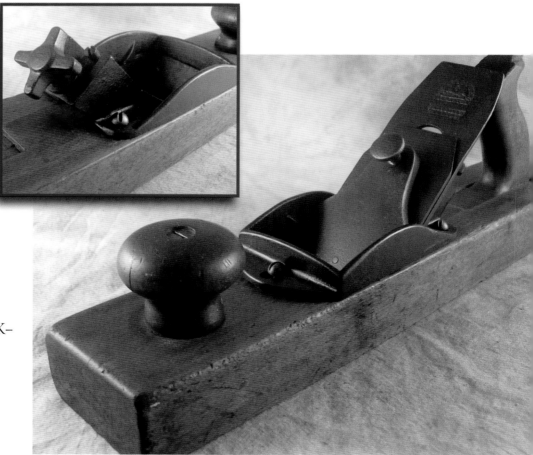

Pike Fore Plane

Inventor: Asahel Pike

Origin: Pittsburgh, Pennsylvania

Patent Number & Date: 161,213; March 23, 1875.

Iron fore plane 18" lg x 2 3/4" w.
Double iron 2 1/4" w, not marked.

Chaplin Patent Planes

Inventor: Orril R. Chaplin

Origin: Boston, Massachusetts

Patent Number & Date: 126,519; May 7, 1872 (Basic Patent).

Beech handled smooth plane 10" lg x 3" w. Iron 2 1/4" w. Both iron and toe stamped "CHAPLIN'S PATENT MAY 7, 1872." Manufactured by Tower & Lyon. Plated cap iron and blade adjuster.

Inventor: Orril R. Chaplin

Origin: Boston, Massachusetts

Patent Number & Date: 126,519; May 7, 1872.

Beech handled smooth plane 9 1/4" lg x 2 5/8" w.
Cutter 2" w. Both cutter and toe stamped
"CHAPLIN'S PATENT MAY 7, 1872."
"Manufactured by Tower & Lyon."

Chaplin Patent Planes *Continued*

Inventor: Orril R. Chaplin

Origin: Boston, Massachusetts

Patent Number & Date:
126,519; May 7, 1872 (Basic Patent).

Beech handled jack plane 15" lg x 2 3/4" w. No marks.
Toe stamped "CHAPLIN'S PATENT MAY 7, 1872."
"MFD BY TOWER & LYON." Chrome plated iron cap
and blade adjuster. .

Inventor: Orril R. Chaplin

Origin: Boston, Massachusetts

Patent Number & Date: 126,519; May 7, 1872.

Iron jack plane 15 3/16" lg x 2 1/2" w. Single iron 2 1/8" w, stamped "O.R. CHAPLIN'S PATENT PAT'D MAY 7, '72". Brass handle and knob nickel plated. Smooth bottom. Engraved lever.

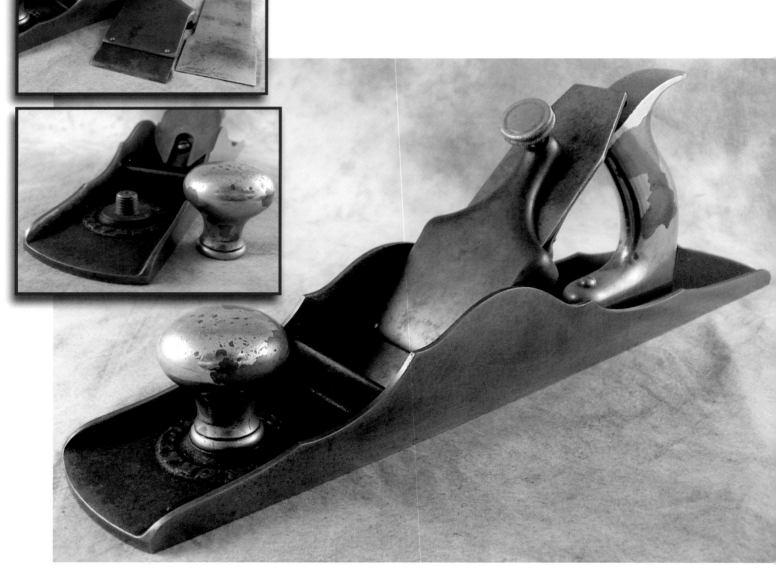

Chaplin Patent Planes *Continued*

Inventor: Orril R. Chaplin

Origin: Boston, Massachusetts

Patent Number & Date: 126,519; May 7, 1872.

Iron smooth plane (below), 8 7/8" lg x 2 1/8" w. Iron 1 3/4" w, marked "TOWER & LYON" with Chaplin's patent dates. "NO. 4" cast on bed. "O.R. CHAPLIN'S PATENT" cast around front knob. Iron handle and knob.

Iron smooth plane (right), 8 3/16" lg x 2 1/16" w. Cutter 1 5/8" w. No marks. Adjustable throat. iron handle and knob.

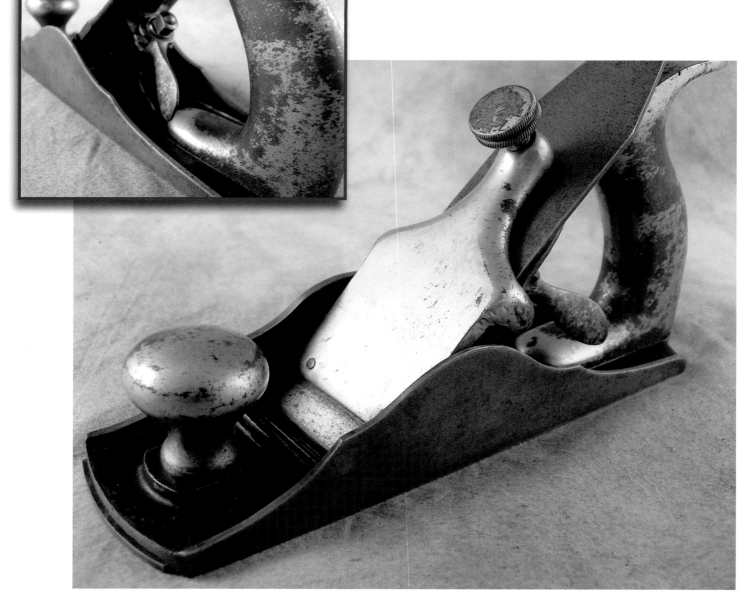

Chaplin
Patent Planes *Continued*

Inventor: Orril R. Chaplin

Origin: Boston, Massachusetts

Patent Number & Date: 126,519; May 7, 1872.

Iron smooth plane 9" lg x 2 5/16" w. Cutter 2" w, marked "CHAPLIN'S PAT. TOWER & LYON, NEW YORK, MAY 7, 72, JULY 4, 76." Adjustable throat, hard rubber handle.

Inventor: Orril R. Chaplin

Origin: Boston, Massachusetts

Patent Number & Date: Circa 1888.

Iron block plane. Adjustable throat. Steel cap iron has two "yokes" for securing blade. No ribbed top.

Inventor: Orril R. Chaplin

Origin: Boston, Massachusetts

Patent Number & Date: Circa 1888.

Iron block plane 6 1/2" lg x 1 7/8" w. Single iron marked "O.R. CHAPLIN'S PAT. NEW YORK." "TOWER & LYON, MAY 7 '72 -JULY 4 '76." Fixed throat corrugation on top only for strength.

Inventor: Orril R. Chaplin

Origin: Boston, Massachusetts

Patent Number & Date: Circa 1890.

Iron block plane. Throat not adjustable. Wood knob, plated straight-sided cap iron. Ribbed top and blade, lateral adjuster. "A" casting on frog.

Chaplin
Patent Planes *Continued*

Inventor: Orril R. Chaplin

Origin: Boston, Massachusetts

Patent Number & Date: 1898; 1899; 1900; 1902.

Iron smooth plane 8 1/2" lg x 2" w. Cutter 1 3/4" w, marked "CHAPLIN'S IMPROVED PATENT. TOWER & LYON, NEW YORK, MAY 7, 72, JULY 4, 76." Adjustable throat. "NO. 1233" cast on bed. Painted wood knob and checkered hard rubber handle.

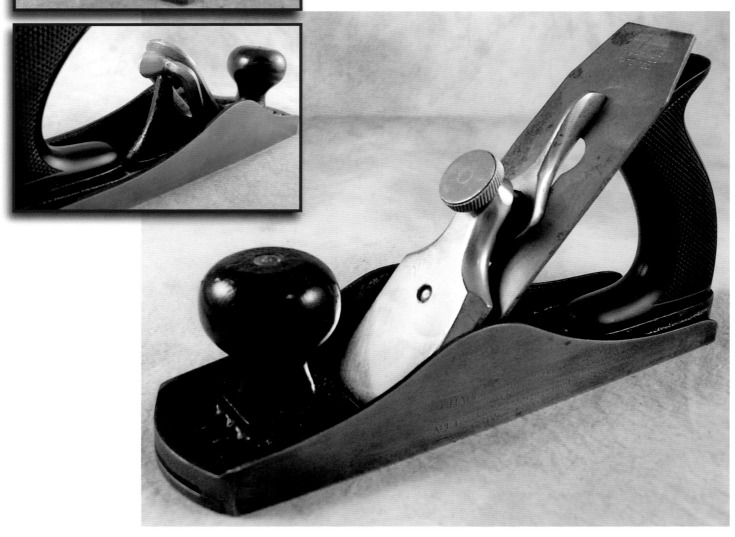

Inventor: Orril R. Chaplin

Origin: Boston, Massachusetts

Patent Number & Date: 1898; 1900; 1902.

Iron jack plane 15" lg x 2 1/2" w. Cutter 2 1/8" w.
"CHAPLIN'S IMPROVED" cast around front knob.
Wood knob and checkered rubber handle.

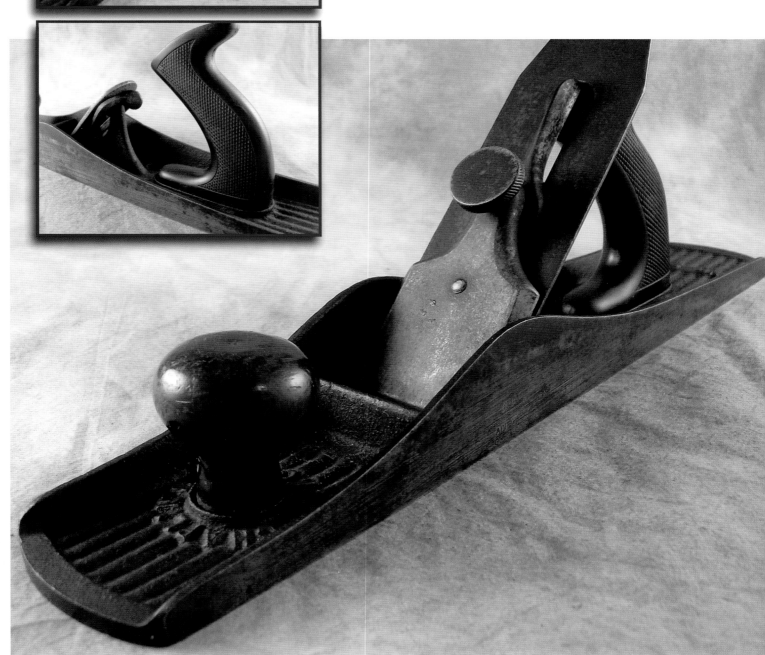

Tidey Beveling Plane

Inventor: M. B. Tidey

Origin: Dundee, New York

Patent Number & Date: 11,235; July 4, 1854.

Tidey's Double Beveling Plane. Beech with brass trim. One 1 1/4" iron on each side piece. Plane marked "M.B. TIDEY & CO. - DUNDEE, N.Y." and "PAT'D JULY 4, 1854". Plane cuts a bevel on corners of a workpiece with one pass. Patent issued to M.J. Wheeler, H. W. Pierce, C. W. Rogers and M. B. Tidey. Top brass plate stamped "M.B. Tidey & Co. Dundee, New York." Patent number and date stamped on curved brass beveling gauge.

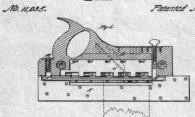
Wheeler, Rogers, Pierce & Tidey,
Bench Plane.
No. 11,035.   Patented July 4, 1854.

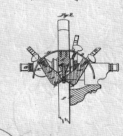

Spotlight Plane

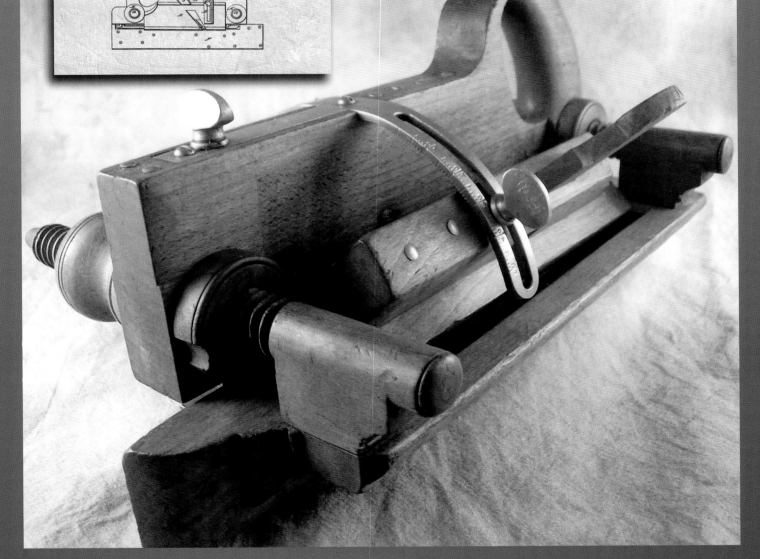

Scientific American.

THE ADVOCATE OF INDUSTRY, AND JOURNAL OF SCIENTIFIC, MECHANICAL, AND OTHER IMPROVEMENTS.

VOLUME X.]

NEW-YORK MARCH 17, 1855.

[NUMBER 27.

THE
SCIENTIFIC AMERICAN,
PUBLISHED WEEKLY
At 128 Fulton Street, N. Y. (Sun Buildings,)
BY MUNN & COMPANY.

O. D. MUNN.   S. H. WALES.   A. E. BRACH.

Agents.

Federhen & Co., Boston.   Dexter & Bro., New York.
Stokes & Bro., Philadelphia.   S. G. Fuller, Halifax, N. S.
S. G. Courtenay & Co.,Charleston. S. W. Pease, Cincinnati, O.
Avery Bedford & Co., London.   M. M. Gardissal & Co., Paris.

Responsible Agents may also be found in all the principal cities and towns in the United States.

Single copies of the paper are on sale at all the periodical stores in this city, Brooklyn and Jersey City.

TERMS—$2 a-year.—$1 in advance and the remainder in six months.

Railway Economy in Construction and Repair.

One of the great mistakes of railway construction has been in consequence of the inordinate desire to open the works at the very earliest day. To such an extent has this hurry been carried, that many of our companies have laid down their iron without proper ballasting, and with the road-bed in such a condition that it could not resist the action of severe rains or frosts of the climate. Then, again, the iron has been taken from the importer without survey or examination, and experience has shown that in many cases much of the iron has had to be taken up and replaced in three or four years, when, in fact, had it been of proper quality, it would have lasted twenty years. Then, again, the sleepers have been laid down without kyanizing or other chemical preparation, to preserve them, and they have to be renewed in from three to five years ; when, had they been properly prepared, they would have lasted from fifteen to twenty-five years; and almost every other department of construction has been carried on with like wastefulness and indiscretion. Let our readers examine the annual reports of the different companies they are interested in, or familiar with, particularly with regard to the per centage of annual repairs, and see if our remarks are not well grounded. Owing to this kind of management, many of our railroads are now passing their dividends.— [American Railway Times (Boston).

Beans for Soup.

The use of beans as an article of food, is not so considerable as it should be. Beans are the most nutritious of all kinds of food used by man. Chemical analysis, and the experience of those who make extensive use of them, demonstrate this. To make good bean soup, take one quart of white beans and a shank beef bone and boil all together for two hours, then add salt and pepper for seasoning. The use of bones is not so much esteemed as they should be in food. By boiling them in soup some of the phosphate of lime, which goes to form our bones, is taken up and we thus get a supply of a necessary element for our bodies which cannot be obtained so fully from roasted or fried meat.

Gold near Reading, Pa.

Dr. C. M. Wetherill has confirmed his former announcement of the discovery of gold near Reading. The gold was discovered by Mr. Philipps, a mining geologist, searching for iron ore, a few miles westward from Reading, and on the farm of Mr. Entlich, also on the western slope of Penn's Mount. It was obtained in washing specimens of ferruginous quartz.

Liberal Employers.

On February 8th, the Directors of the Bank of England notified their employees that they would receive a bonus of ten per cent. on their salaries, in consequence of the present high price of provisions.

IMPROVED BEVEL PLANES.

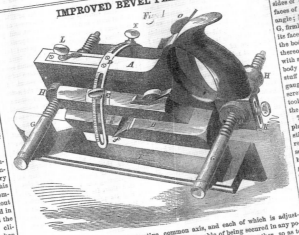

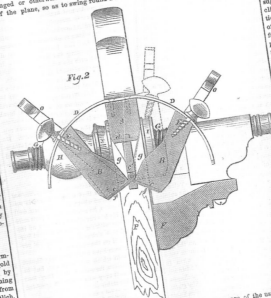

The annexed engravings are a perspective view, figure 1, and a transverse section, figure 2, of an improvement in beveling planes, for which a patent was granted to M. J. Wheeler, G. W. Rogers, H. W. Pierce, and M. B. Tidey, of Dundee, N. Y., on the 4th of July last.

The object of this invention is to plane a double bevel, or in other words, to plane a two faces at any desired angle to each other and to a third face. The invention consists in attaching the two cutters, which are to plane the two faces, to two wings which are both hinged or otherwise attached to the body of the plane, so as to swing round a common axis, and each of which is adjustable and capable of being secured in any position independently of the other, so as to bring and set the faces of the cutters at any angle to each other, or to the fence which is employed to guide the plane.

A is the body of the plane ; B B are the wings which contain the cutters, $f f$, and are connected to the underside of the body, A, by a three-flanged hinge, $c c c'$, figure 2. One flange, c', of this hinge, is inserted in the body, A, and secured by screws, $d d$. The screws are secured one to each of the faces of the wings, B B, and all are united by a pin running the whole length of the wings. The wings are shorter than the body, A, and a recess equal in length to the wings, is cut in each side of the latter, to allow them to lay up close to the sides of it, and bring their faces and the edges of their cutters as nearly as is desirable in the same plane. The cutters are of the usual form, and secured in the wings by wedges, O O, in the usual way. The wings swing within a bar, D, which is in the form of part of a circle described from the axis, and are secured in any position by means of set screws, E E, passing through slots, in the bar, D, and

screwing into their backs. The upper surface of the bar, D, is graduated in degrees, commencing in both directions from the sides of the body, A, in order to enable the faces of the wings to be set at any desired angle ; F is the fence having the screws, G G, firmly attached to it, perpendicularly to its face ; said screws pass through holes in the body, and being furnished on one side thereof with a nut, H, and on the other side with a follower, I, to adjust the fence to the body and wings, for the purpose of planing staff of various widths ; K is the depth gauge which is adjusted by means of the screws, L M, for the purpose of enabling the tool to cut to the required depth to perfect the bevel, and no further.

The operation of the plane can be best explained by illustrating the beveling of a door stile on opposite sides of the channel which receives the panel. The stile, P, is represented in figure 2. The fence, F, is adjusted by the screws, G G, to bring the depth of gauge to the proper distance from the side of the stile. The wings are adjusted to set the edges of the cutters at the proper angle to each other and to the face of the stile, and the depth gauge is set to the proper depth. The edge of the stile is then planed down till the depth gauge comes in contact with the bottom of the groove. If it be desired the two sides of the channel may have different bevels, as each wing with its cutter is adjustable independently of the other. By making the edge of the cutters of this plane of proper form, coves, ovolos, ogees, or moldings of any other form may be produced on the edges of the stuff.

More information may be obtained by letter addressed to M. B. Tidey & Co., Dundee, N. Y. The planes are manufactured by this company.

Sugar Manufacture of France.

France is the largest producer of beet sugar in the world. A favorable soil and climate, and a rural and industrious population, contribute to the successful prosecution of the beet sugar manufacture. This manufacture originated during the reign of Napoleon Bonaparte. His continental system raised colonial produce to an almost fabulous price. The high rate of sugars induced many to look around for the means of producing sugar at home, and an impetus was given to the search, by the offer of a magnificent premium by the emperor to the successful discoverer of a permanent home source of supply. Of all the plants tried the beet proved the most promising, but forty years elapsed before the manufacture of beet sugar was enabled to cope successfully with colonial sugars. From France the culture spread through Belgium, Germany, and far into the interior of Russia, and now there is produced of this kind of sugar on the continent of Europe three hundred and sixty millions of pounds, nearly one-half of which is manufactured in France, in three hundred and thirty-four manufactories. In the vicinity of Lille the average yield of the sugar beet is sixteen tuns to the acre, and at Valenciennes nineteen tuns. In some localities twenty-five tuns are produced.

New Potato Digger.

The St. Paul Daily Times (Minesota) describes a new machine for digging potatoes, invented by F. Jones, to which the attention of farmers in that region is directed. It is calculated for two horses, and will dig about five acres in a day.

A submarine iron boat has been built in this city in order to go down and secure the treasure said to have been lost with the British frigate Hussar, in Hurl Gate.

Carpenter Patent Planes

Inventor: Emanuel W. Carpenter

Origin: Lancaster, Pennsylvania

Patent Number & Date: 5,807X; January 30, 1830.

Patented tongue plane with adjustable iron feature.
Split adjustable iron. Cutting width locked by means of two screws.
Slide arm adjustable fence. 13 5/8" lg x 8" w.

Inventor: Emanuel W. Carpenter

Origin: Lancaster, Pennsylvania

Patent Number & Date: 6,226; March 27, 1849.

Beech jack plane 16" lg x 3" w. Single iron 1 5/8" w. stamped "W. BUTCHER". Wood wedge secures blade.

Carpenter
Patent Planes *Continued*

Inventor: Emanuel W. Carpenter

Origin: Lancaster, Pennsylvania

Patent Number & Date: 6,226; March 27, 1849.

Beech block plane 8 3/8" lg x 3 1/8" w. Double iron 2 1/4" w, stamped "W. BUTCHER WARRANTED". Wood wedge secures blade.

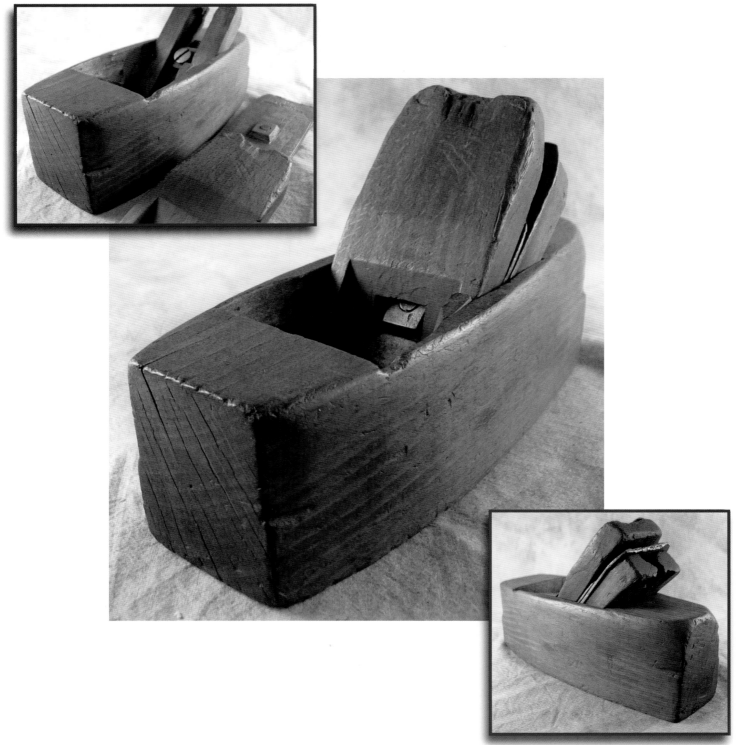

Inventor: Samuel Auxer

Origin: Lancaster, Pennsylvania

Patent Number & Date:
Circa 1860 - 1882.

E.W. Carpenter's style
smooth plane 11 1/2" lg x 3" w.
Double iron stamped
"W. BUTCHER".
Wood wedge blade lock.

Carpenter Patent Planes *Continued*

Inventor: I. Carpenter

Origin: Lancaster, Pennsylvania

Patent Number & Date: 81,425; August 25, 1868.

Wood bottom iron top jack plane (below). Selective iron framing on top strengthens knob and handle. This design reduces plane weight compared to a full iron top. Thumb screw secures cap iron with a double wedge like that of E.W. Carpenter's March 27, 1849 patent for adjusting plane mouth. Toe stamped "I CARPENTER #81,425 AUG 25,1868 LANCASTER PA."

Wood bottom iron top patented transitional jack plane (right). The fancy open iron work top designed for aesthetics, strength and for reduction of weight vs. a full iron top. Thumb screw secures cap iron with a double wedge feature like that of E.W. Carpenter's patent #6,226; March 27, 1849.

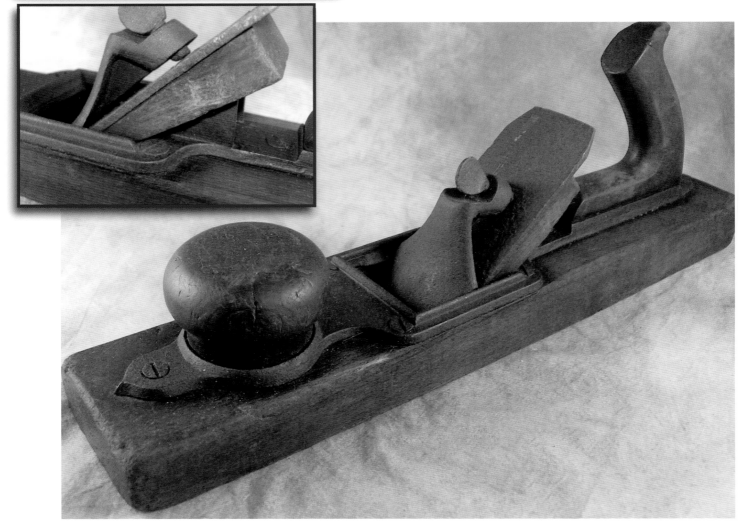

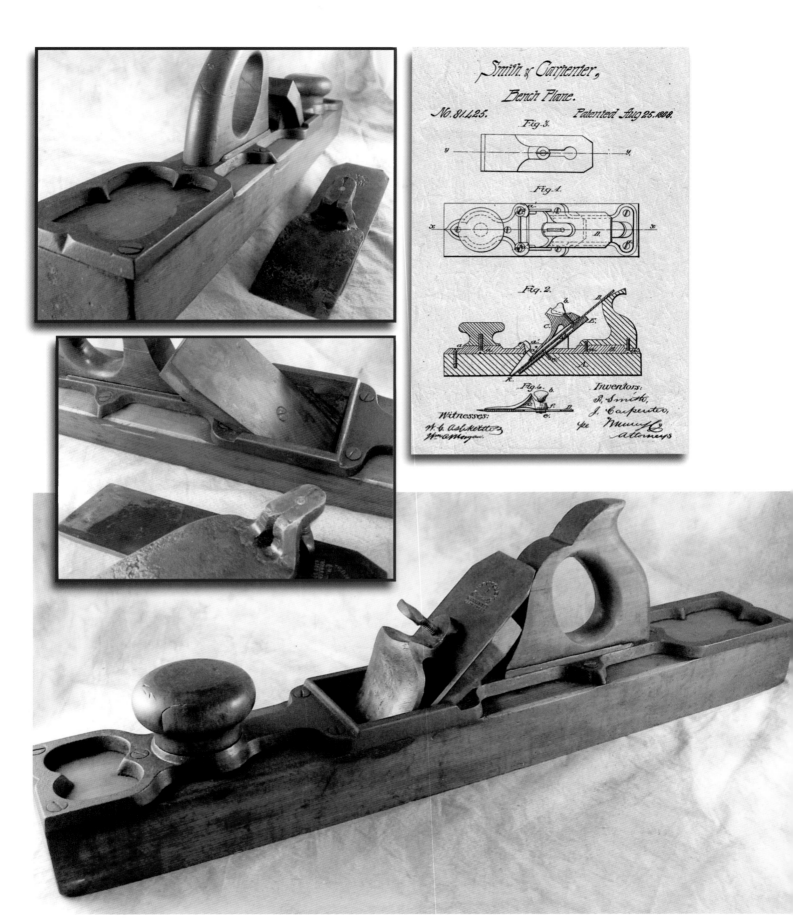

Simons Jack Plane

Inventor: James Y. Simons

Origin: Troy, New York

Patent Number & Dates:
84,140; November 17, 1868.

Iron jack plane 9 3/4" lg x 2 1/4" w.
Single cutter 1 3/4" w, no marks.
Wood handle and knob. "J.Y.S. PAT
NOV. 17, 68" cast on lever cap.

Eclipse Jack Plane

Inventor: Eclipse Plane Company

Origin: Coshocton, Ohio

Patent Number & Dates:
315,014; April 7, 1885.

Patents: James Duncan & William H. Talbot -
Buchanan, Michigan assigned to J. Duncan,
William W. Bostwick & Frank C. Hay,
all of Coshocton, Ohio. Manufactured version
made under patent #315,014. Patent info
cast in plane body behind front knob. Basic
design patent #157,162 November, 24, 1874.

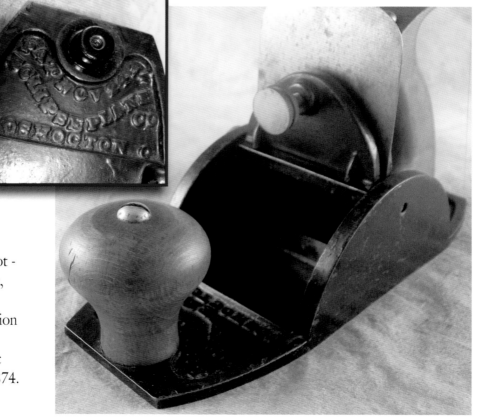

Foster Smooth Plane

Inventor: Edwin W. Foster

Origin: Central Park, New York

Patent Number & Date: 842,453; January 1907.

Foster's turn-table iron smooth plane. 9 3/4" lg x 2 11/16" w. Thick tapered double iron 2" w. Marked "OHIO TOOL COMPANY." Beech handle and knob stained and grain painted. Has lateral adjustment. Patent date cast on bed.

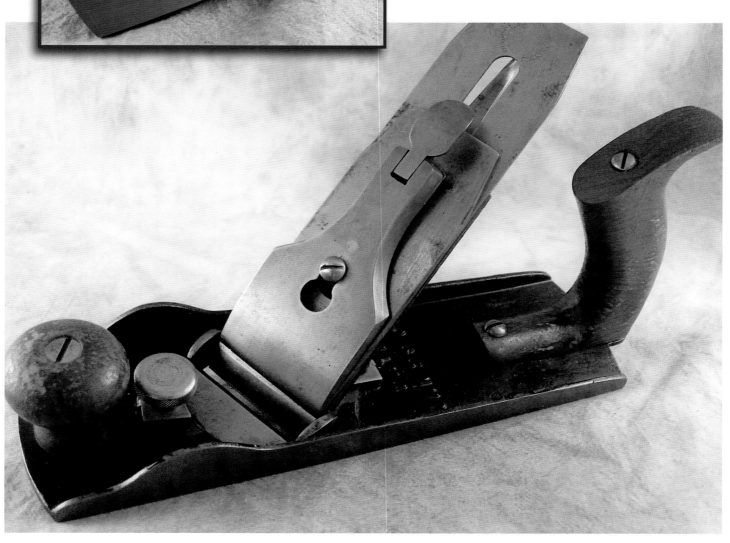

Buckeye Patent Planes

Inventor: John Muehl

Origin: Cleveland, Ohio

Patent Number & Date: 775,378; November 22, 1904.

Iron smooth plane (at right in group photo below, also closeup photos at left). 9 1/2" lg x 2 1/4" w. Single iron 2" w, no marks. "PAT. NOV. 22, 04" cast in rear of bed. Wood handle engraved with "wheat" pattern. Wood knob, corrugated bottom.

Iron jack plane (at left in group photo below, also closeup photos at right). 14" lg. x 2 5/16" w. Single iron 2" w, no marks. "BUCKEYE 5" cast at toe of plane, "PAT NOV. 22, 04" cast in rear of bed. Wood knob and wood handle engraved with a "wheat" pattern. Corrugated bottom.

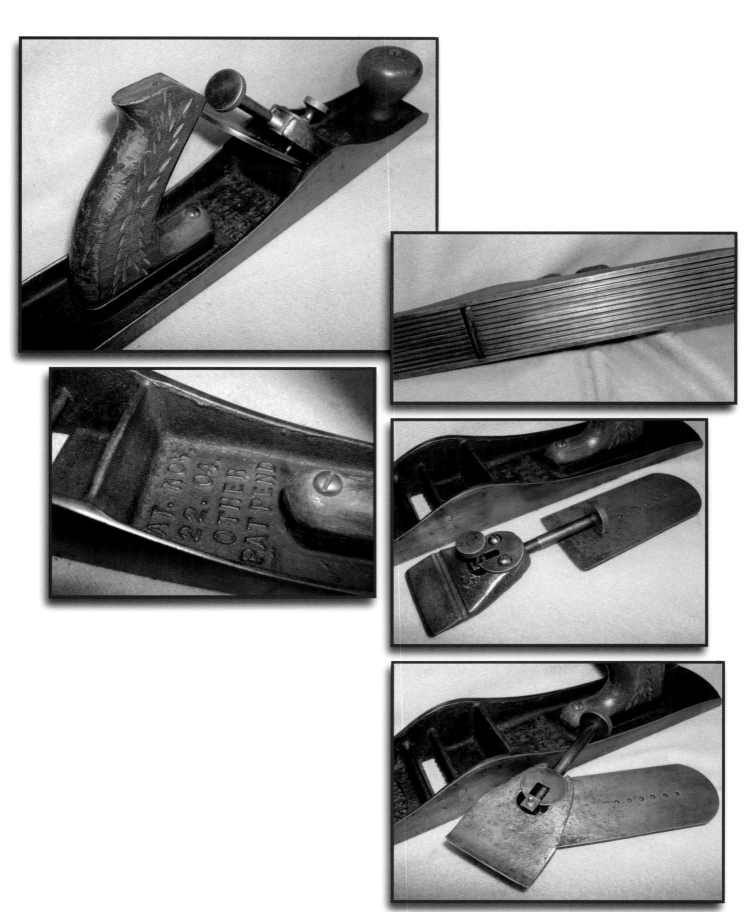

Buckeye
Patent Planes *Continued*

Inventor: John Muehl

Origin: Cleveland, Ohio

Patent Number & Date: 775,378; November 22, 1904.

Iron smooth plane 9 1/2" lg x 2 3/8" w. Single iron marked "NORVELL SHAPLEIGH HARDWARE CO. DIAMOND EDGE". Circa 1910. Toe cast "DE-04C PAT 22, 04" John Muehl patent.

Cross Jointer Plane

Inventor: A. S. Cross

Origin: Ripon, Wisconsin

Patent Number & Date: 33,240; September 10, 1861.

Wood jointer with adjustable fence. Brass adjusting plate on each end of fence to set the desired pitch. Two brass screws lock fence in place. Toe and heel marked "PAT. SEPT 10, 1861 O. PASKO".

Metallic Plane Co.
Metal Planes

Inventor: Metallic Plane Company

Origin: Auburn, New York

Patent Number & Date: No Known Patents.

Iron filletster plane (below), 10 1/2" lg x 2 3/4" w. Skewed cutter 2" w, marked "EXCELSIOR CUTTER-METALLIC PLANE CO, AUBURN, NY." Rack and pinion cutter adjustment.

Iron filletster plane (right), 10 1/2" lg x 3 1/2" w. Single iron 2" w, marked "EXCELSIOR". Rosewood knob and handle. Decorated fence. Iron secured by a screw.

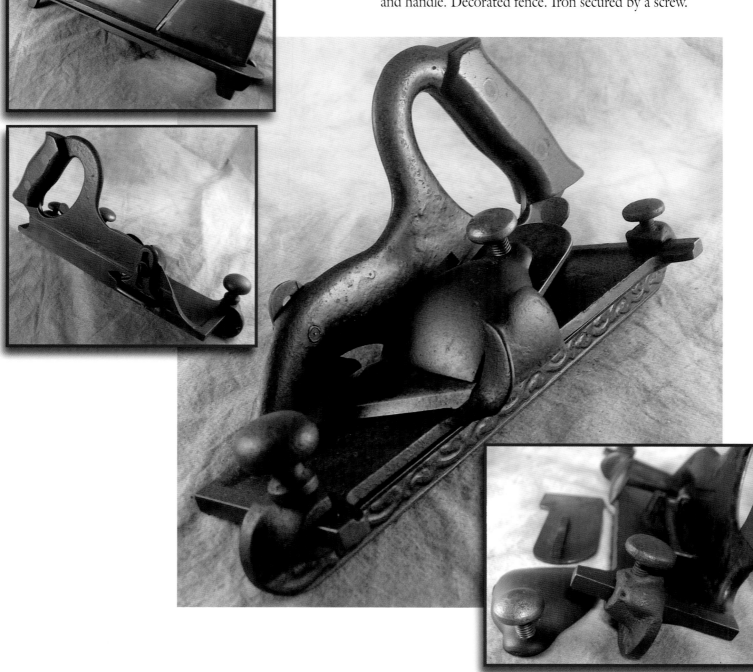

Metallic Plane Co.
Metal Planes *Continued*

Inventor: Metallic Plane Company

Origin: Auburn, New York

Patent Number & Date: Unknown.

Iron block plane No. 8 (right), 7 3/16" lg x 2 1/16" w. Single iron 2" w, marked "EXCELSIOR CUTTER-METALLIC PLANE CO, AUBURN, NY." Adjustable throat. Rack & pinion type cutter adjustment. Iron knob. Plane side marked "METALLIC PLANE CO - AUBURN, NY. PATENTED."

Iron block plane No. 9 (below), 7 3/4" lg x 2 3/8" w. Single iron 2" w, unmarked. Iron knob and adjustable throat. Wood grip piece attached to rear top of iron. Rack and pinion type cutter adjustment. "METALLIC PLANE CO, AUBURN, NY" stamped on side.

Inventor: Metallic Plane Company

Origin: Auburn, New York

Patent Number & Date: No Known Patent.

Iron block plane No. 7 (right),
5 15/16" lg x 2" w. Single iron 1 9/16" w.
Marked "EXCELSIOR CUTTER-
METALLIC PLANE CO, AUBURN, NY."
Rack & pinion type cutter adjustment.
No front knob. No marks on side.

Iron block plane (below),
7 3/16" lg x 2 1/16" w. Single iron marked
"EXCELSIOR CUTTER-METALLIC
PLANE CO, AUBURN, NY."
Adjustable throat. Metal knob and cap.
Rack & pinion type cutter adjustment.

Metallic Plane Co.
Metal Planes *Continued*

Inventor: Metallic Plane Company

Origin: Auburn, New York

Patent Number & Date: Unknown.

Block plane. Small wood palm rest on blade.
Single iron 1 1/2" w. Iron marked
"EXCELSIOR CUTTER METALLIC PLANE CO.
AUBURN NY". 5 1/2" lg x 1 3/4" w. Wood
wedge secures iron.

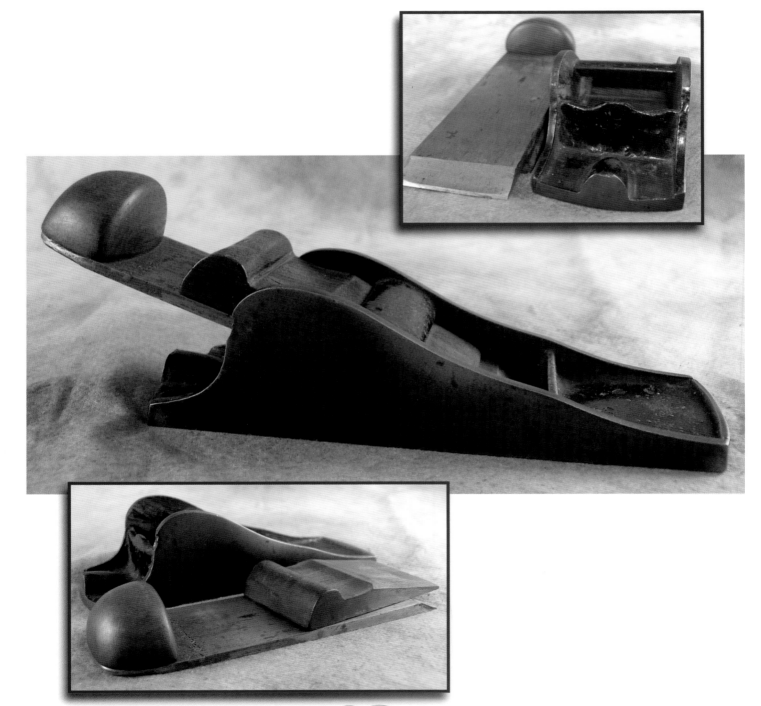

Ripsom Mitre Plane

Inventor: Joseph B. Ripsom

Origin: Oshkosh, Wisconsin

Patent Number & Date: 296,785; April 15, 1884.

Carriagemaker's iron mitre plane 11" lg x 2 3/16" w. Sole and double iron 1 1/4" w, no marks. Walnut handle and knob. Brass adjustment nut. Plane owner's name stamped on side of handle, "Albert E. Giese".

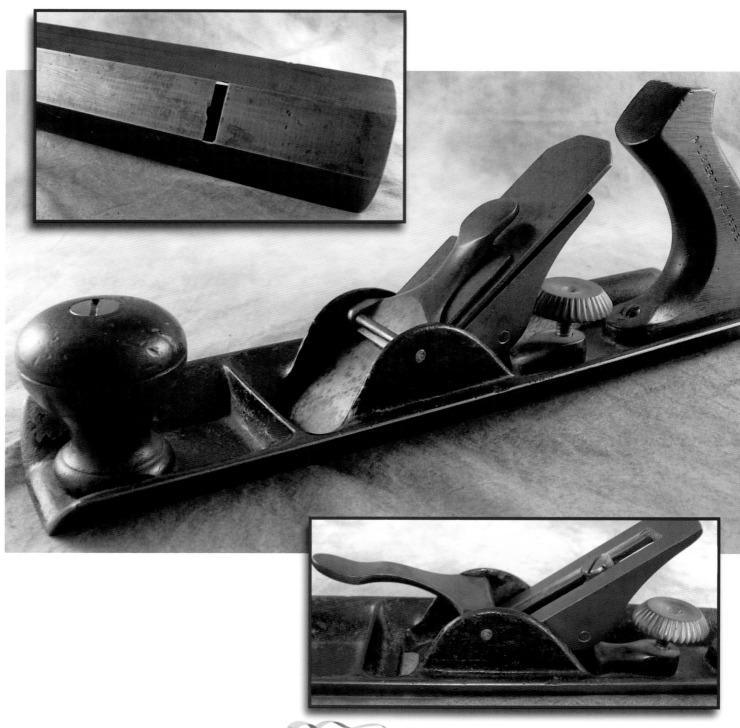

Hardt Smooth Plane

Inventor: Louis Hardt

Origin: Yuba City, California

Patent Number & Date: 502,906; August 8, 1893.

Iron smooth plane. Bailey type adjustment feature. Adjustable front nose piece that is locked by a thumb screw in front of knob. Lever cap, frog and cutter are Sargent components. 11 5/8" lg x 2 11/16" w. Rosewood knob and handle. Patent info on toe.

Blandin Jointer Plane

Inventor: Benjamin A. Blandin

Origin: Charlestown, Massachusetts

Patent Number & Date: 64,477; May 7, 1867.

No. 7 size iron plane 22" lg x 2 3/8" w. Iron lever cap with thumb screw blade lock. Rocker type adjustment feature with vertical adjuster. Brass adjuster wheel marked with patent date.

Palmer Patent Planes

Inventor: Metallic Plane Company

Origin: Auburn, New York

Patent Number & Date: 64,790; May 14, 1867.

Iron jack plane (below), 15" lg x 2 7/16" w. Single iron stamped with "clover leaf" trade mark. Beech handle and knob. "METALLIC PLANE CO. - AUBURN, N.Y." cast in toe end. "PALMER'S PATENT MAY 14, 1867" cast into bed at the heel end. Nelson Palmer Auburn, N.Y. patent assigned to self and S.W. and J.F. Palmer.

Iron smooth plane (right), 10" lg x 2 3/8" w. with stamped "clover leaf" trade mark. Wood handle and knob. Corrugated sole and adjustable throat. Nelson Palmer patent assigned to self and S.W. and J.F. Palmer.

Palmer
Patent Planes *Continued*

Inventor: Metallic Plane Company

Origin: Auburn, New York

Patent Number & Date: 121,406; November 28, 1871.

Iron smooth plane 8 1/2" lg x 2 1/2" w. Double iron 2" w, marked "CHARLES BUCK". Corrugated bottom, adjustable throat. Wood handle and knob. Non-adjustable. "PALMER & STORKE'S - METALLIC PLANE CO, AUBURN, NEW YORK" stamped on side. Patented by Sidney W. Palmer & Elliot G. Storke.

Inventor: Metallic Plane Company

Origin: Auburn, New York

Patent Number & Date: 162,710; April 27, 1875.

Wood bottom jack plane 14 1/2" lg x 2 3/4" w. Iron 2 1/8" w, marked "EXCELSIOR CUTTER-METALLIC PLANE CO, AUBURN, NY." Beech stock & handle. Metal casting 11" lg on top of wood base. Original paper label on side. Elliot Storke's 1875 patent.

Palmer
Patent Planes *Continued*

Inventor: Metallic Plane Company

Origin: Auburn, New York

Patent Number & Date: 174,870; March 14, 1876.

Iron jack plane (below), 15" lg x 2 3/8" w. Double iron 2" w, marked "OHIO TOOL CO." Iron cap with thumb screw. Iron knob and wood handle. Corrugated bottom. "METALLIC PLANE CO., AUBURN, N.Y. PATENT" stamped on side. Elliot G. Storke patent.

Iron fore plane (right), 20 7/8" lg x 2 3/8" w. Double iron 2 3/8" w, marked "OHIO TOOL." Brass cap most likely not original. Corrugated bottom, adjustable throat. Metal knob and wood handle. Side marked "METALLIC PLANE CO., AUBURN, NY PAT."

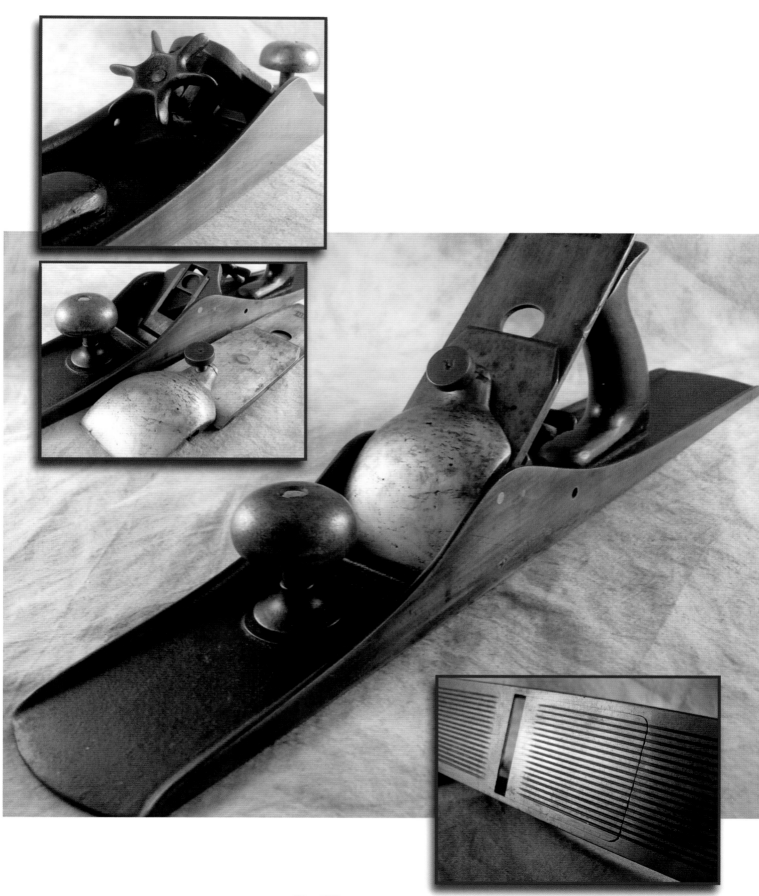

Piper
Plow Plane

Inventor: Samuel A. Piper

Origin: Newton Upper Falls, Massachusetts

Patent Number & Date: 43,398; June 28, 1881.

Piper's patent plow plane with rosewood frame and wedge. Brass arms and depth stop. Full length fence swings down on the same principle as the fence arms. Brass medallion inset into the side of the fence. Medallion marked with S.A. Piper's address and patent date.

Spotlight Plane

Siegley
Patent Planes

Inventor: Jacob Siegley

Origin: Wilkes-Barre, Pennsylvania

Patent Number & Date: 510,096; December 5, 1893.

Iron fore plane 19 5/8" lg x 2 3/4" w. Single iron marked "SIEGLEY PAT DEC 3, 1893." "No. 10" cast on lever cap. No lateral adjustment. Beech handle and knob with light checkered design on handle.

Hahn
Bench Planes

Inventor: Edwin Hahn

Origin: Wilkes-Barre, Pennsylvania

Patent Number & Date: Siegley Patents (basically).

Smooth plane made by Edwin Hahn. 9 1/2" lg x 2 3/8" w.
Single thick iron. Corrugated bottom with lateral
adjustment. Plane marked No. 2 rear of front knob.
"Hahn" appears twice in rear on each side of tote.
Relationship to Siegley unknown.

Hahn
Bench Planes *Continued*

Inventor: Edwin Hahn

Origin: Wilkes-Barre, Pennsylvania

Patent Number & Date: Circa 1910.

Iron smooth plane (below), 9 3/4" lg x 2 1/2" w. Iron marked "EDWIN HAHN MANF'R" and rear of cap iron. Corrugated bottom and checkered wood handle. Hahn planes nearly identical to Siegley planes. Relationship unknown.

Iron jack plane (right), 13 15/16" lg x 2 5/16" w. Single iron 2" w, no markings. "NO 5" cast on plane base. Corrugated bottom and checkered wood handle. Hahn planes nearly identical to Siegley planes. Relationship unknown.

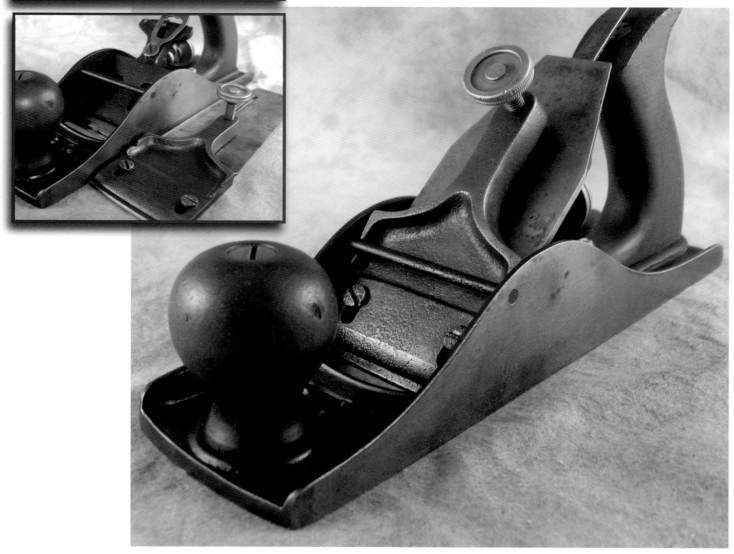

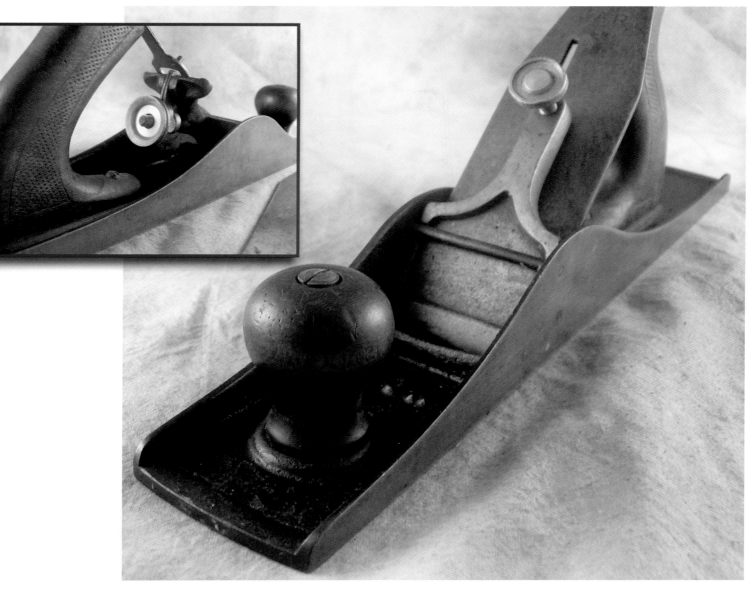

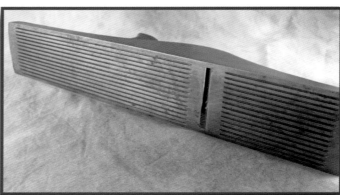

Davis Patent Planes

Inventor: Davis Level and Tool Company

Origin: Springfield, Massachusetts

Patent Number & Date: 122,339; January 2, 1872.

Charles Torrance patent January 2, 1872, Holyoke, Massachsetts. Iron smooth plane 8 3/4" lg x 2 3/8" w. Double iron marked "MOULSON BROS." Beech handle and knob.

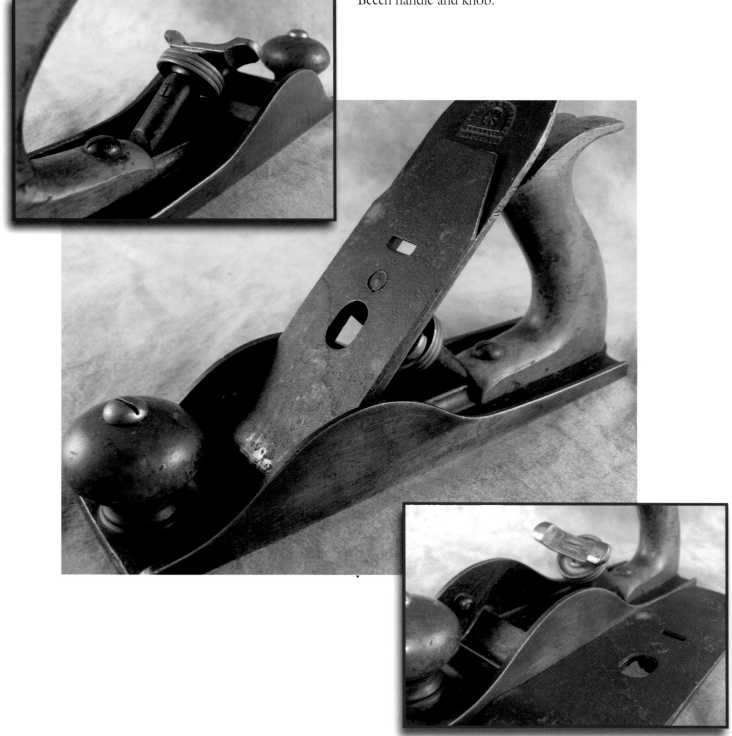

Inventor: Davis Rule and Level Company

Origin: Springfield, Massachusetts

Patent Number & Date: 167,311; August 31, 1875.

Iron Jack Plane 15" lg x 2 1/2" w. Double iron, no marks. Rosewood handle and knob. Gold paint stripe around frog base.

Davis
Patent Planes *Continued*

Inventor: Davis Level & Tool Company

Origin: Springfield, Massachusetts

Patent Number & Date: 167,311; August 31, 1875.

Iron smooth plane (below), 8 3/4" lg x 2 13/16" w. Double iron. Rosewood handle and knob. Gold stripe around frog base. Leonard L. Davis patent.

Iron jointer plane (right), made by Davis Level & Tool Company. 22 7/8" lg. x 2 13/16" w. Double iron. Rosewood handle and front knob. Gold paint stripe around frog base. Leonard L. Davis Patent.

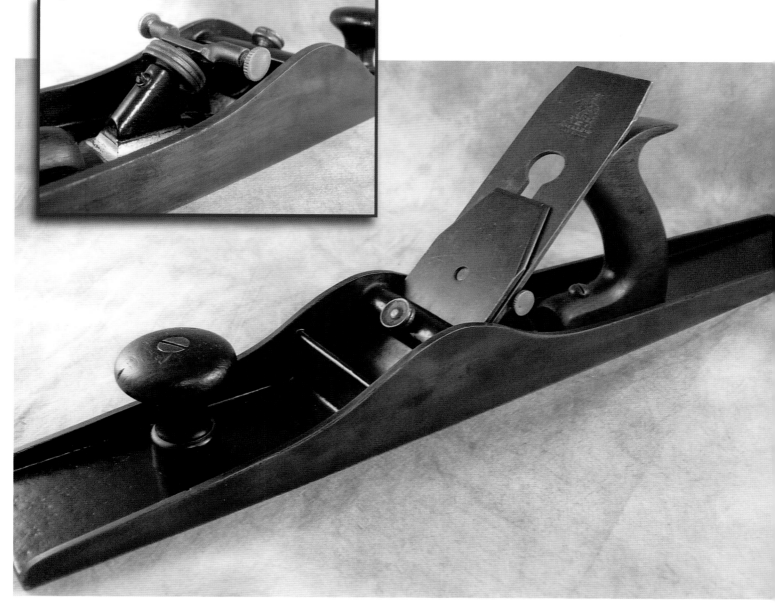

Davis
Patent Planes *Continued*

Inventor: Davis Level & Tool Company

Origin: Springfield, Massachusetts

Patent Number & Date: No Known Patent.

Iron block plane 6 1/16" lg x 1 13/16" w.

Single iron 1 1/2" w. No marks.

Brass thumb screw secures blade. No stenciling.

Leonard L. Davis *1838-1908*

Sandusky Tool Co. Smooth Plane

Inventor: Sandusky Tool Company

Origin: Sandusky, Ohio

Patent Number & Date:
1,696,384; December 25, 1928.

Sandusky plane No. 3SC. Patented by Wilbur Schere.
9" lg x 2 3/8" w. Blade 2" w. Owner's initials on plane, "OJS".
Blade marked "SANDUSKY TOOL CO. USA
ESTABLISHED 1868".

Bundy
Combination Plane

Inventor: Lewis Bundy

Origin: Moores Forks, New York

Patent Number & Date: 109,174; November 18, 1870.

Combination match and plow plane 18" lg x 7 3/4" w, including arms. Three beech sections. Closed handles from one piece of cherry. Skate on plow thumb screws and wear plate on top of arms are brass. "L. BUNDY COMB'D MATCH PLANE & PLOW PAT'D NOV. 15, 1870 MOORESFORKS, N.Y." hand stamped on brass nameplate.

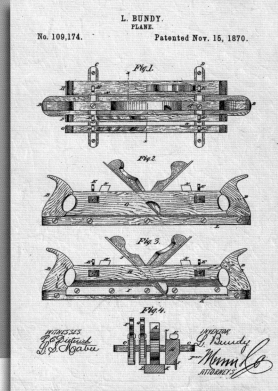

L. BUNDY'S
COMB'D
MATCH PLANE
& PLOW
PAT'D NOV.15 1870
MOORES FORKS.
N.Y.

Spotlight
Plane

Union Mfg. Co. Patent Planes

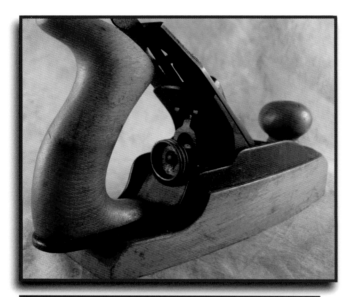

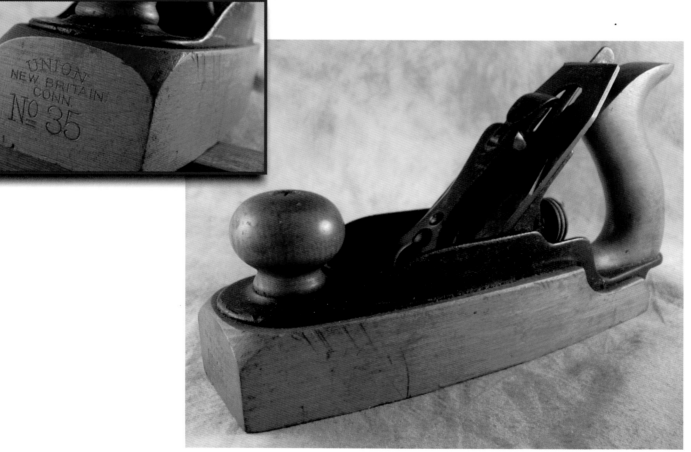

Inventor: Union Manufacturing Company

Origin: New Britain, Connecticut

Patent Number & Date:
746,285; December 8, 1903 &
763,721; June 28, 1904.

Wood bottom iron top smooth plane similar to Stanley No. 35 plane. 9" lg x 2 5/8" w. Double iron 2" w, marked "UNION MANUFACTURING CO. NEW BRITAIN USA." Open tote. Toe stamped "No. 35 UNION MANUFACTURING CO. NEW BRITAIN CONN." George E. Trask and John W. Carleton, New Britain, Connecticut.

Inventor:
Union Manufacturing Company

Origin: New Britain, Connecticut

Patent Number & Date:
December 8, 1903 – October 22, 1889.

Wood bottom jack plane 15" lg x 2 3/4" w.
Double iron 2 1/8" w, marked
"UNION MFG CO. USA." Locking
lever adjustment. No. X-27. Patent dates
stamped on toe.

Union Mfg. Co.
Patent Planes *Continued*

Inventor: Union Manufacturing Company

Origin: New Britain, Connecticut

Patent Number & Date:
746,285; December 8, 1903 & 763,721; June 28, 1904.

Iron jack plane 14" lg x 2 7/16" w. Double iron 2" w, marked "UNION MFG CO USA." Mahogany handle and knob. Rear of cap iron marked "4". Vertical post blade adjusting and locking feature. John W. Carleton and George E. Trask patents.

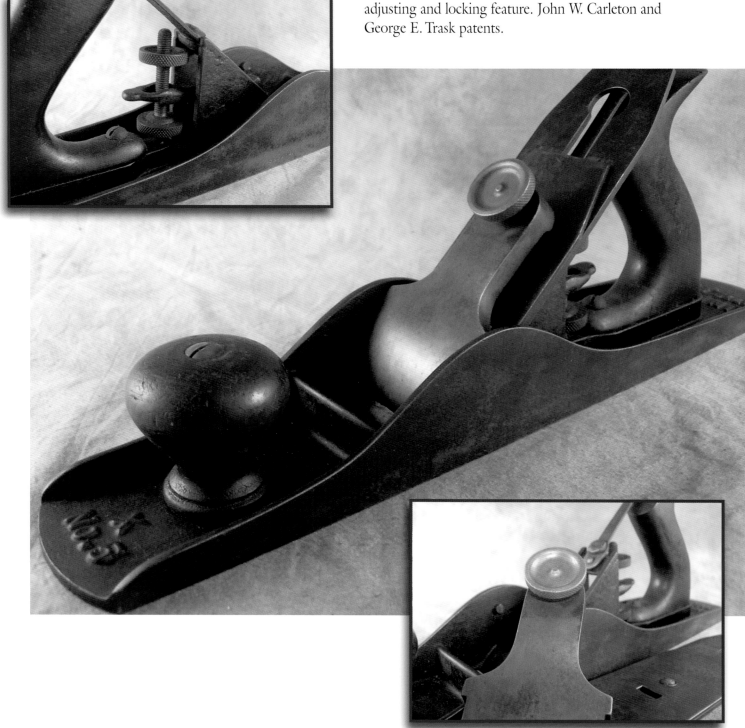

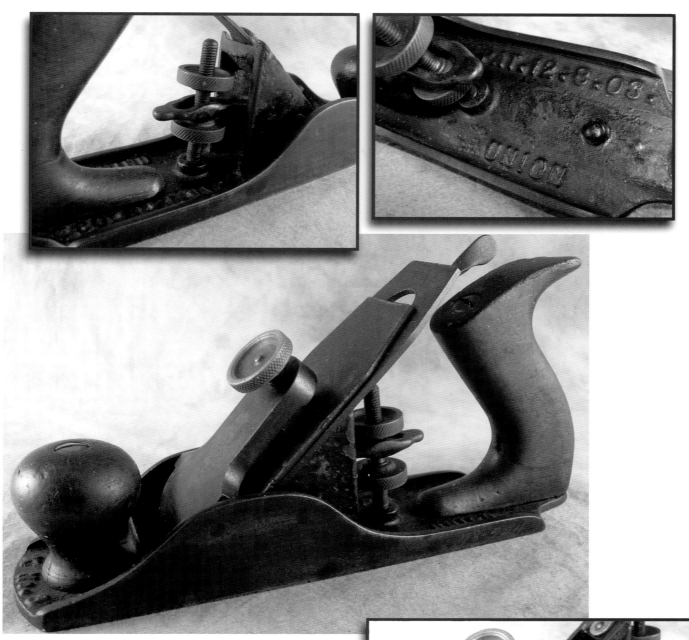

Inventor: Union Plane Company

Origin: New Britain, Connecticut

Patent Number & Date: 763,721; June 28,1904.

Iron smooth plane 8" lg x 2 1/8" w. Double iron 1 3/4" w, marked "UNION MFG CO USA. 12-8-1903" cast on plane bed. Mahogany knob and handle. Rear of cap iron marked "3". The vertical threaded post with two brass adjustment nuts control and lock the arm which in turn adjusts the cutter. Toe stamped No. 3.

Union Mfg. Co.
Patent Planes *Continued*

Inventor: Union Manufacturing Company

Origin: New Britain, Connecticut

Patent Number & Date:
Patent Applied For, Circa 1905.

Block plane Union 9 3/4 with detachable rear rosewood handle. Throat adjustment accomplished by moving the sliding throat piece. Adjuster stamped "PATENT APPLIED FOR". Blade stamped "UNION MANUFACTURING COMPANY NEW BRITAIN, CONN."

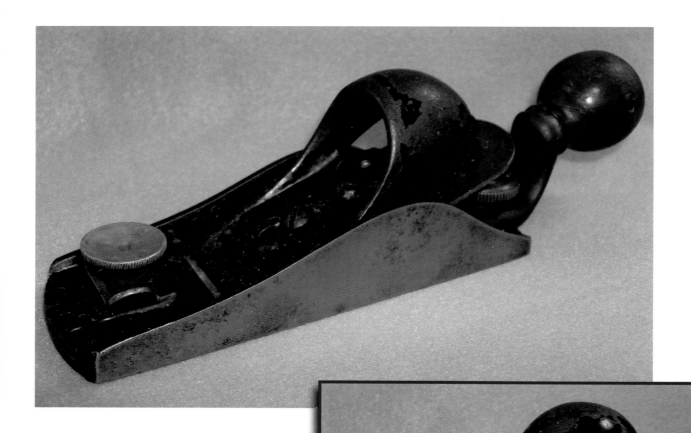

Inventor: Union Manufacturing Company

Origin: New Britain, Connecticut

Patent Number & Date: Circa 1904, None Known.

Iron fore plane 18 1/8" lg x 2 11/16" w. Traces of "UNION MFG. CO. - PAT. OCT. 22 1889" can be seen on cutter. Handle and knob stained mahogany color. "UNION NO. 6" cast on bed at heel. Plane has a unique direct drive screw adjustment feature. "PAT. APPL'D FOR" stamped on lateral adjustment lever.

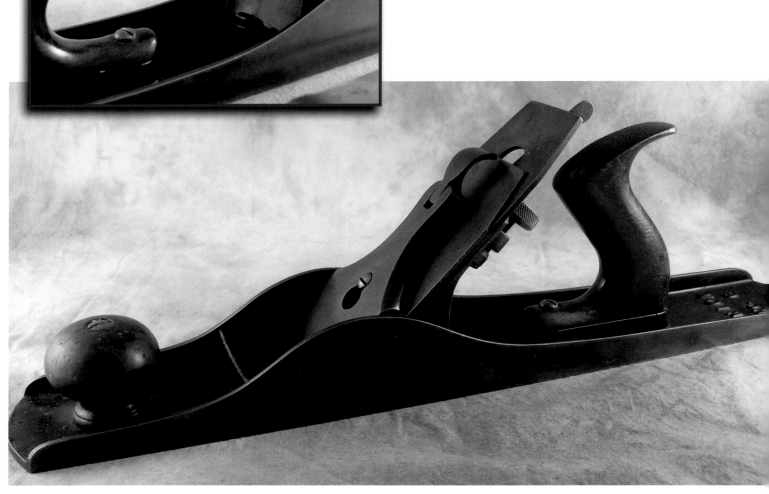

Heald Planes

Inventor: Addison Heald

Origin: Milford, New Hampshire

Patent Number & Date: Circa 1873.

Single boxed bead plane made by Addison Heald of Milford, New Hampshire. Toe marked "A.J. WILKINSON & CO." Wilkinson was a large hardware dealer in Boston, Massachusetts. Many Addison Heald-made planes have this hardware dealer's stamp. 9 1/2" lg x 1 1/8" w. Wood wedge with iron thumb screw secures blade.

Inventor: Addison Heald

Origin: Milford, New Hampshire

Patent Number & Date: Circa 1870.

Block plane 6 1/2" lg x 2" w. Made by Addison Heald of Milford, New Hampshire. Wood wedge and thumb screw secures blade.

Upson Patent Planes

Inventor: Upson Nut Company

Origin: Unionville, Connecticut

Patent Number & Date: 410,710; September 10, 1889.

Wood bottom smooth plane No. 36. Double iron.
Blade stamped "UPSON NUT".

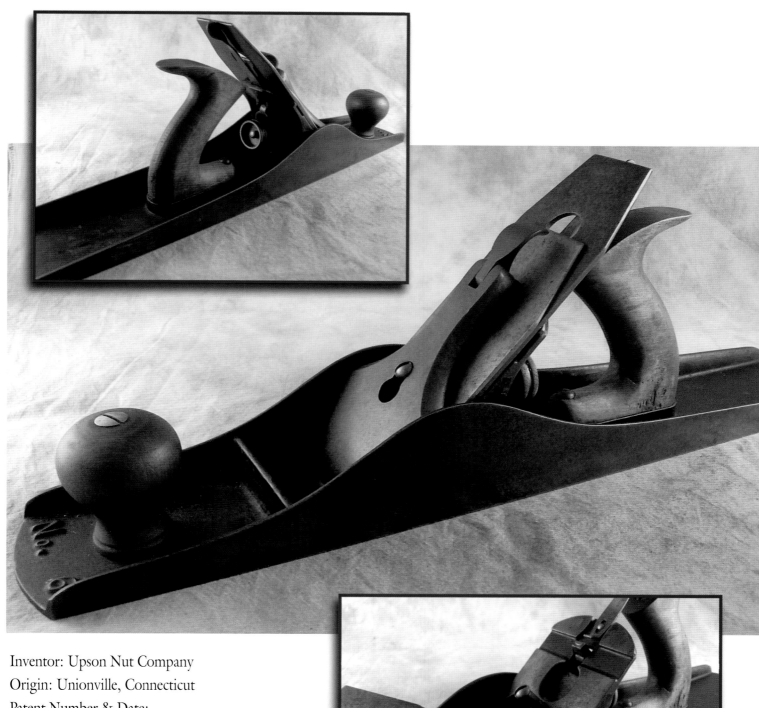

Inventor: Upson Nut Company

Origin: Unionville, Connecticut

Patent Number & Date:
410,710; September 10, 1889.

Fore plane 17 9/16" lg x 2 7/8" w. Double iron
2 15/16" w, marked "UPSON NUT CO."
"No. 6" cast in base at toe. Patented
by George Karrmann; assigned to Upson
Nut Company.

Jensen Combination Plane

Inventor: Conrad Jensen

Origin: Boston, Massachsetts

Patent Number & Date: 126,707; May 14, 1872.

Combination dado, rabbet, and filletster plane. Single iron rosewood body and handle. Boxwood screw arms and lock nuts. Main body with single skewed iron 2" wide. Second body 1 1/2" wide with single iron. "C. JENSEN PAT'D MAY 14, 1872" stamped on toe. Plane manufactured by J. H. Lamb New Bedford Massachusetts, circa 1872-73.

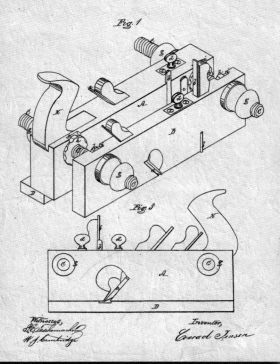

CONRAD JENSEN.
Improvement in Planes.

No. 126,707.   Patented May 14, 1872.

Fig.1

Fig.3

Witnesses,   Inventor,
                              Conrad Jensen

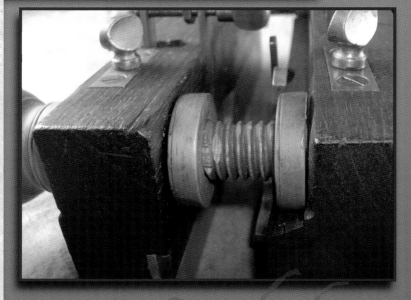

Windsor Beaders

Inventor: Windsor Beader

Origin: Windsor, Vermont

Patent Number & Date: 319,161; June 2, 1885.

Windsor hand beader (this page, top). Type 2.
Patented by Orlando E. Williams and Lawrence V. Poole.

Windsor hand beader, second type (this page, bottom).
Hardwood frame and handles japanned with brass tips.
Brass plate and fence on sole with brass frame to
support multiple cutter heads. 10 1/2" lg.
Orlando E. Williams and Lawrence Poole, Windsor, Vermont.

Inventor: Windsor Beader

Origin: Windsor, Vermont

Patent Number & Date: 313,617; March 10, 1885.

First model marked "PATENT PENDING". Cherry wood frame, brass tips.
Multiple heads with steel thumbscrew. 9 1/2" lg. Patent application dated
November 28, 1884. First model made between this date and March 10, 1884.
Patented by L.V. Poole & O.E. Williams.

Inventor: Windsor Beader

Origin: Windsor, Vermont

Patent Number & Date: 326,435; September 15, 1885.

Windsor hand beader. Third type. Nickel plated steel frame. Turned hardwood
handles japanned black. Beader came with multiple cutters for various profiles.
Patented by Elton P. Kendall and Ambrose S. Vose, Windsor, Vermont..

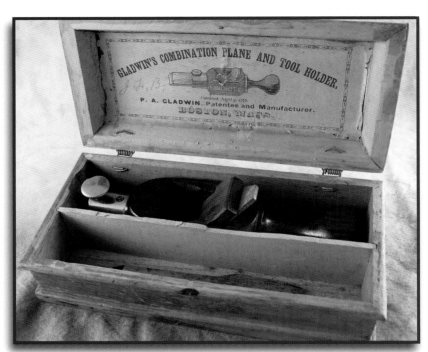

Gladwin Patent Planes

Inventor: Porter A. Gladwin

Origin: Boston, Massachusetts

Patent Number & Date: 202,105; April 9, 1878.

Porter Gladwin's patented combination plane and tool handle Rosewood body with nickel plated ferrules and thumb screw. This tool is in its original wooden box with a selection of interchangeable tools. Advertising label glued on inside cover of wood box lid.

Inventor: Porter A. Gladwin

Origin: Boston, Massachusetts

Patent Number & Date: 202,105; April 9, 1878.

Nickel plated combination plane and tool handle equipped with an adjustable cutter seat that changes the pitch of the iron. "P. A. GLADWIN" cast on lever cap, "PAT. APR. 9, 1878 - BOSTON" cast inside base.

Standard Rule Patent Planes

Inventor: The Standard Rule Company

Origin: Unionville, Connecticut

Patent Number & Date: 287,584; October 30, 1883.

The Standard Rule Company No. 24 smooth plane (below). Wood bottom, rosewood knob with cast iron hand palm rest.

Wood jack plane (right), 15" lg x 2 3/8" w. Double iron 2" w, marked "THE STANDARD RULE CO PATENTED OCT 30, 1883 UNIONVILLE, CT." Toe stamped "UPSON NUT CO. No. 26, UNIONVILLE, CONN."

Standard Rule
Patent Planes *Continued*

Inventor: The Standard Rule Company

Origin: Unionville, Connecticut

Patent Number & Date: 287,584; October 30, 1883.

Iron block plane 7" lg x 2" w. No.13. Single iron 1 3/4" w. marked "THE STANDARD RULE CO. PATENTED OCT 30, 1883 UNIONVILLE, CT."

Inventor: The Standard Rule Company

Origin: Unionville, Connecticut

Patent Number & Date: 287,584; October 30, 1883.

Iron smooth plane, No. 3 size. Rosewood handle and knob. Double iron. Blade stamped "THE STANDARD RULE CO. PATENT OCT. 30, 1883." Patent held by Solon Rust, Pine Meadows, Connecticut.

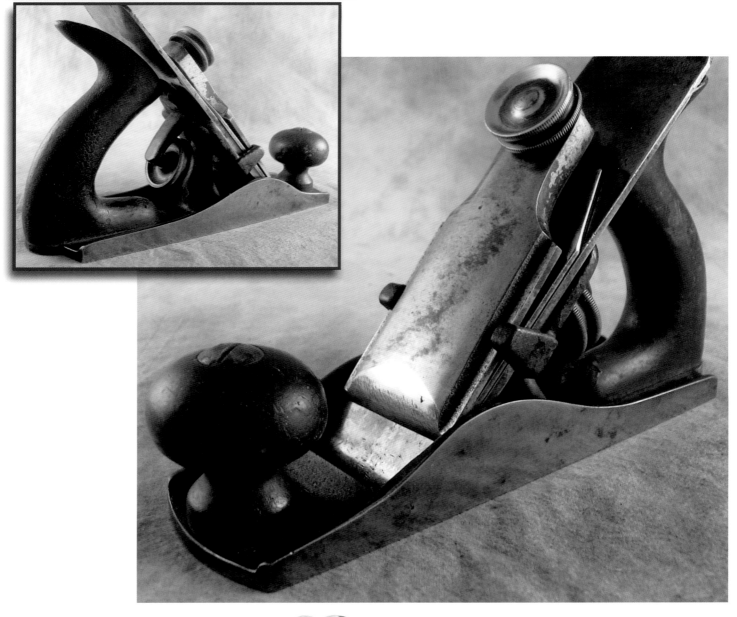

Bridges-Gage
Patent Plane

Inventor: D.A. Bridges

Origin: Vineland, New Jersey

Patent Number & Date: 271,569; January 30, 1883.

Patented wood body plane. Earliest patented plane associated with the Gage Tool Company. David Bridges assigned three quarters of patent to John Gage.

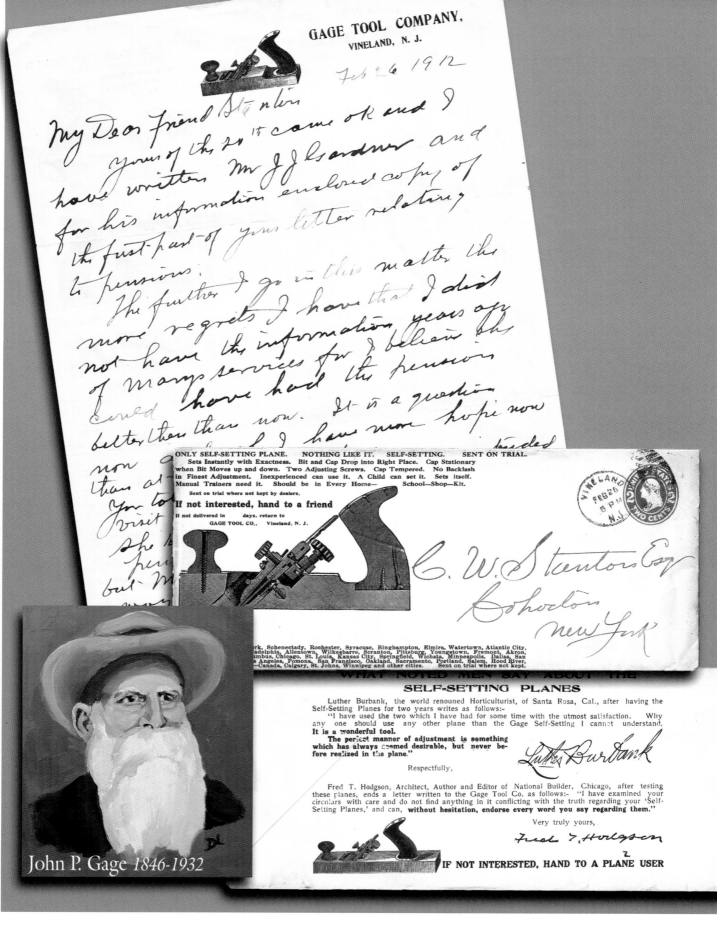

GAGE TOOL COMPANY,
VINELAND, N. J.

Feb 26 1912

My Dear Friend Stanton

Yours of the 20th came ok and I have written Mr J J Gardner and for his information enclosed copy of the first part of your letter relating to pensions.

The further I go in this matter the more regrets I have that I did not have the information years ago of Marys services for I believe she would have had the pension better then than now. It is a question now _____ I have more hope now than at _____

You told _____ visit _____ she _____ pension _____ but M _____

ONLY SELF-SETTING PLANE.   NOTHING LIKE IT.   SELF-SETTING.   SENT ON TRIAL.
Sets Instantly with Exactness. Bit and Cap Drop into Right Place. Cap Stationary when Bit Moves up and down. Two Adjusting Screws. Cap Tempered. No Backlash in Finest Adjustment. Inexperienced can use it. A Child can set it. Sets itself. Manual Trainers need it. Should be in Every Home—   School—Shop—Kit.

Sent on trial where not kept by dealers.

If not interested, hand to a friend

If not delivered in   days, return to

GAGE TOOL CO.,   Vineland, N. J.

C. W. Stanton Esq
Cohocton
New York

VINELAND FEB 26 8 PM N.J.

...rk, Schenectady, Rochester, Syracuse, Binghampton, Elmira, Watertown, Atlantic City, ...adelphia, Allentown, Wilkesbarre, Scranton, Pittsburg, Youngstown, Fremont, Akron, ...umbus, Chicago, St. Louis, Kansas City, Springfield, Wichata, Minneapolis, Dallas, San ...s Angeles, Pomona, San Francisco, Oakland, Sacramento, Portland, Salem, Hood River, ...Canada, Calgary, St. Johns, Winnipeg and other cities.   Sent on trial where not kept.

WHAT NOTED MEN SAY ABOUT THE

SELF-SETTING PLANES

Luther Burbank, the world renowned Horticulturist, of Santa Rosa, Cal., after having the Self-Setting Planes for two years writes as follows:-
"I have used the two which I have had for some time with the utmost satisfaction.   Why any one should use any other plane than the Gage Self-Setting I cannot understand. It is a wonderful tool.
The perfect manner of adjustment is something which has always seemed desirable, but never before realized in the plane."

Respectfully,

Luther Burbank

Fred T. Hodgson, Architect, Author and Editor of National Builder, Chicago, after testing these planes, ends a letter written to the Gage Tool Co. as follows:- "I have examined your circulars with care and do not find anything in it conflicting with the truth regarding your 'Self-Setting Planes,' and can, without hesitation, endorse every word you say regarding them."

Very truly yours,

Fred T. Hodgson

IF NOT INTERESTED, HAND TO A PLANE USER

John P. Gage 1846-1932

Gage Patent Planes

Inventor: Gage Tool Company

Origin: Vineland, New Jersey

Patent Number & Date:
271,569; January 30, 1883
323,804; August 4, 1885
339,872; April 13, 1886.

Smooth plane, beech stock. 9" lg x 2" w. Single iron.
Toe stamped "GAGE TOOL COMPANY VINELAND N.J."

Inventor: Gage Tool Company

Origin: Vineland, New Jersey

Patent Number & Date:
1883; 1885; 1886.

Jointer plane, beech stock, 22" lg x 3 1/8" w. Single iron 2 1/4" w. "NO. 17" stamped on heel. Plane found with a Stearns beveling attachment.

Original Gage Tool Company string tag advertising piece. Tags have been observed attached to Gage wooden box shipping containers.

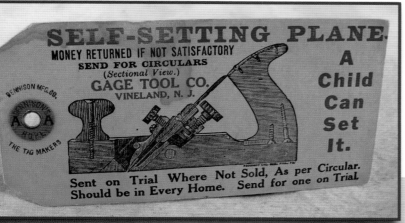

Gage
Patent Planes *Continued*

Inventor: Gage Tool Company

Origin: Vineland, New Jersey

Patent Number & Date:
271,569; January 30, 1883
323,804; August 4, 1885
339,872; April 13, 1886.

Jack Plane, beech stock. 16" lg x 2 3/4" w. Single iron 2" w. "No. 11" stamped on heel. Toe stamped "GAGE TOOL COMPANY VINELAND N.J."

Gage-Stanley Patent Plane

Inventor: Gage - Stanley

Origin: Manufactured by Stanley Rule & Level Company

Patent Number & Date: 1,331,280; February 17, 1920.

Iron smooth plane 9" lg x 2 1/2" w. Single iron 2" w, marked "GAGE SELF SETTING PLANE". Rosewood knob and handle. Remnants of "Stanley" label can be seen on handle. Corrugated bottom. Stanley's third model. Edmund A. Schade Patent.

Erlandsen Mitre Plane

Inventor: J. Erlandsen

Origin: New York

Patent Number & Date: Circa 1890 - 1925.

Low angle iron mitre plane 8 1/8" lg x 2 1/8" w.
Single iron 1 3/4" w, marked "MOULSON BROS."
Nickel plated body and cap. Rosewood infill and
pad fitted to iron. "NO. 6" stamped on toe.

Popping
Shoulder Plane

Inventor: J. Popping

Origin: New York

Patent Number & Date: No Known Patent.

Bronze shoulder plane 6 7/8" lg x 1" w.
Single iron 1" w, stamped "J. POPPING, NY."
Rosewood front knob and pad nicely fitted to the top
of the iron. 3/32" thick steel plate fitted to the sole.
Cap screws similar design motif to Stanley
No. 113 cap screws.

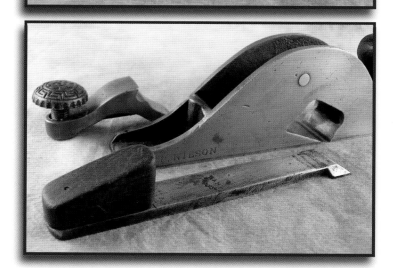

Rodier Bench Planes

Inventor: Louis Rodier

Origin: Westfield, Massachusetts

Patent Number & Date: 212,956; March 4, 1879.

Personal traveling display case includes:
- Iron jack plane 12 1/16" lg x 2 1/16" w.
- Iron smooth plane 8 3/8" lg x 2 1/16" w.
- Iron block plane 6 3/4" lg x 1 13/16" w.
- Iron bullnose block plane 4 5/8" lg x 1 7/8" w.

Rodier Block Plane

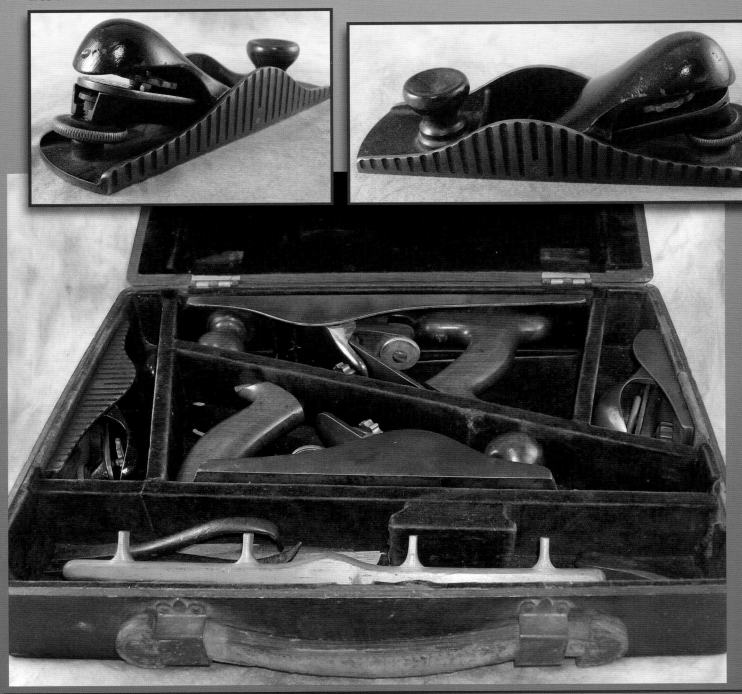

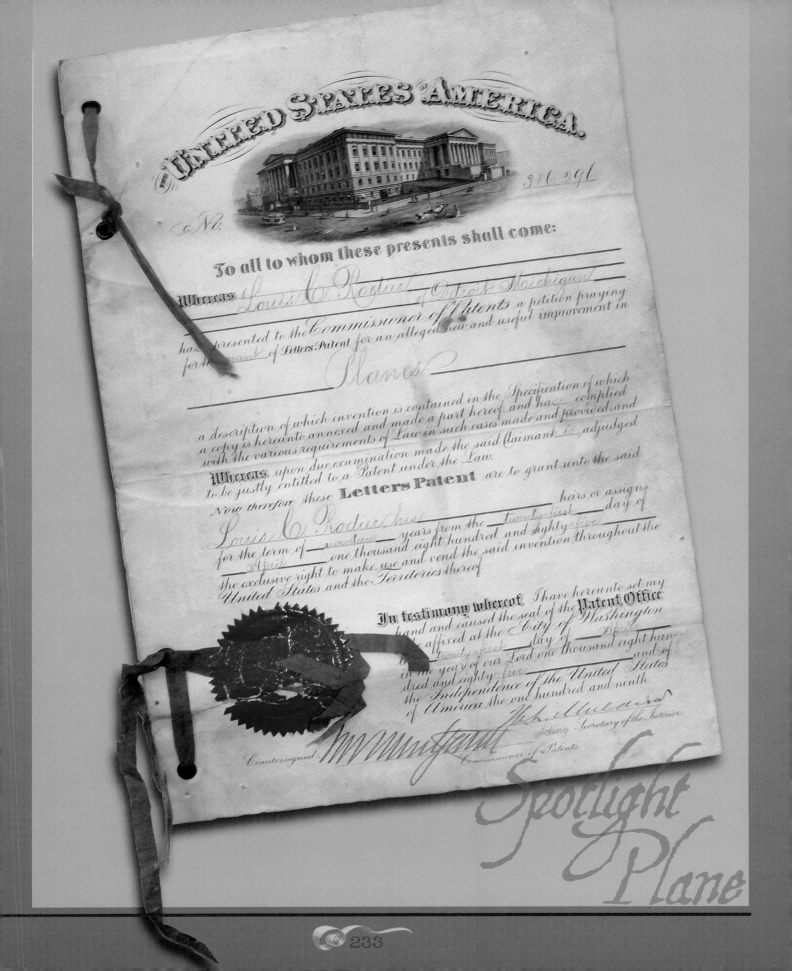

UNITED STATES AMERICA.

No. 316,296

To all to whom these presents shall come:

Whereas Louis C. Roduit of Detroit Michigan

has presented to the Commissioner of Patents a petition praying for the grant of Letters Patent for an alleged new and useful improvement in

Planes

a description of which invention is contained in the Specification of which a copy is hereunto annexed and made a part hereof and has complied with the various requirements of Law in such cases made and provided and

Whereas upon due examination made the said Claimant is adjudged to be justly entitled to a Patent under the Law.

Now therefore these Letters Patent are to grant unto the said

Louis C. Roduit his heirs or assigns for the term of seventeen years from the twenty-first day of April one thousand eight hundred and eighty-five the exclusive right to make, use and vend the said invention throughout the United States and the Territories thereof

In testimony whereof I have hereunto set my hand and caused the seal of the Patent Office to be affixed at the City of Washington this twenty-first day of April in the year of our Lord one thousand eight hundred and eighty-five and of the Independence of the United States of America the one hundred and ninth.

Acting Secretary of the Interior.

Countersigned
Commissioner of Patents.

Rodier
Bench Planes *Continued*

Rodier Smooth Plane

Rodier Bullnose Block Plane

Spotlight Plane

Rodier
Bench Planes *Continued*

Inventor: L.C. Rodier

Origin: Westfield, Massachusetts

Patent Number & Date: 212,956; March 4, 1879.

Iron jack plane 14 1/2" lg x 2 5/8" w. Single 2" iron, stamped "BUCK BROS" with "buck head" logo. Faucet style adjustment knob. Corrugated bottom. Walnut handle and knob. Patent assigned to Laflin Manufacturing Company Co. Westfield, Massachusetts.

Spotlight Plane

Multiform Patent Planes

Multiform Patent Planes

Inventor: Thomas D. Worrall

Origin: Mount Holly, New Jersey

Patent Number & Date: 14,979; May 27, 1856.

Brass top plate plane with detachable handle and moving filletster sole. Multiform Moulding Plane Company offered a complete range of types and size soles popular at the time. Worrall patent date stamped on the heel and handle.

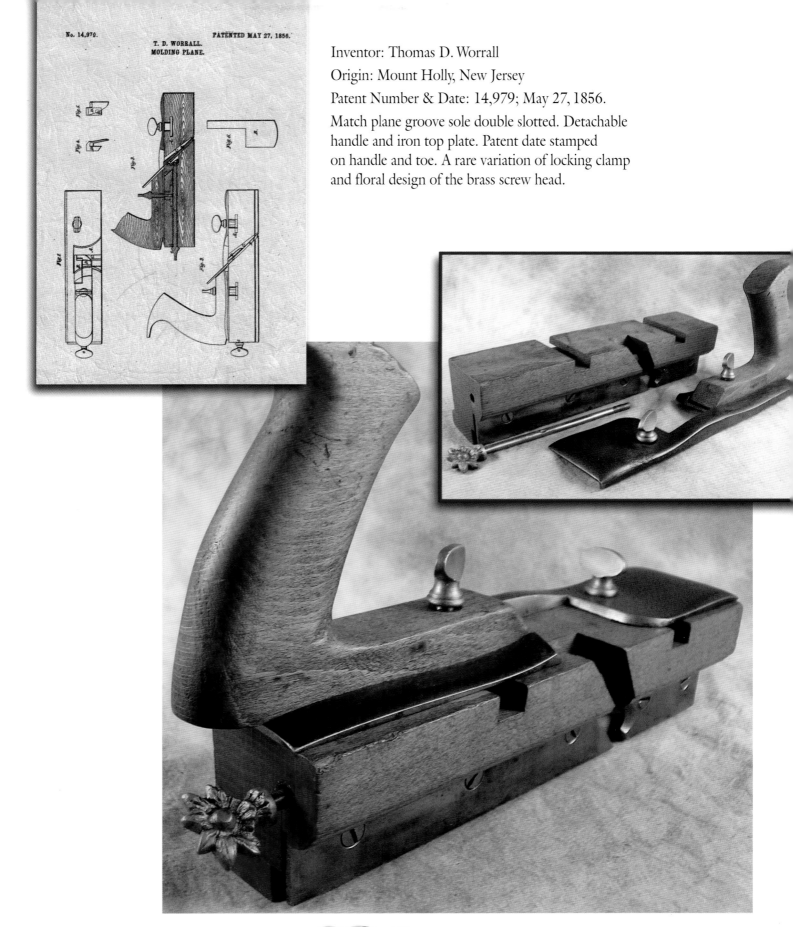

No. 14,979.

T. D. WORRALL.
MOLDING PLANE.

PATENTED MAY 27, 1856.

Inventor: Thomas D. Worrall

Origin: Mount Holly, New Jersey

Patent Number & Date: 14,979; May 27, 1856.

Match plane groove sole double slotted. Detachable handle and iron top plate. Patent date stamped on handle and toe. A rare variation of locking clamp and floral design of the brass screw head.

Multiform
Patent Planes *Continued*

Inventor: Thomas D. Worrall

Origin: Mount Holly, New Jersey

Patent Number & Date: 14,979; May 27, 1856.

Multiform double slotted style plane (below), with full iron top plate and removal handle. Plane shown with a selection of interchangeable double slotted soles.

Worrall's patent plow plane (right). Beech, with boxwood knobs and screw arms. Single slot for detachable handle. Toe marked with Thomas D. Worrall's August 29, 1854 patent. Handle Worrall's patent No. 18,312; September 29, 1857, Lowell, Massachusetts.

Inventor: Thomas D. Worrall

Origin: Mount Holly, New Jersey

Patent Number & Date: 11,635; August 29, 1854.

Adjustable combination plane with handle (left page). Beech stock with boxwood lock nuts and fence. Single iron tongue and groove. Multiform Moulding Plane Company and Worrall's 1854 patent information stamped on toe. P. A. Gladwin June 9, 1857 patent stamped on the lower edge of the toe. Gladwin patent for adjustment feature for different size boards.

Combination match plane (this page). No fence. Two irons for tongue and groove. Toe stamped with Worrall's August 29, 1854 patent information. Gladwin's patent June 9, 1857 stamped on lower edge of toe. Single "T" slot for handle..

Multiform
Patent Planes *Continued*

Inventor: Thomas D. Worrall

Origin: Mount Holly, New Jersey

Patent Number & Date: 11,635; August 29, 1854.

Un-handled ebony plane body with a detachable sole. Two brass locking screws for engaging the "T" shaped slots in each end of the various interchangeable soles. Toe marked "WORRALL MULTIFORM MOULDING PLANE CO. PAT'D AUG 29, 1854".

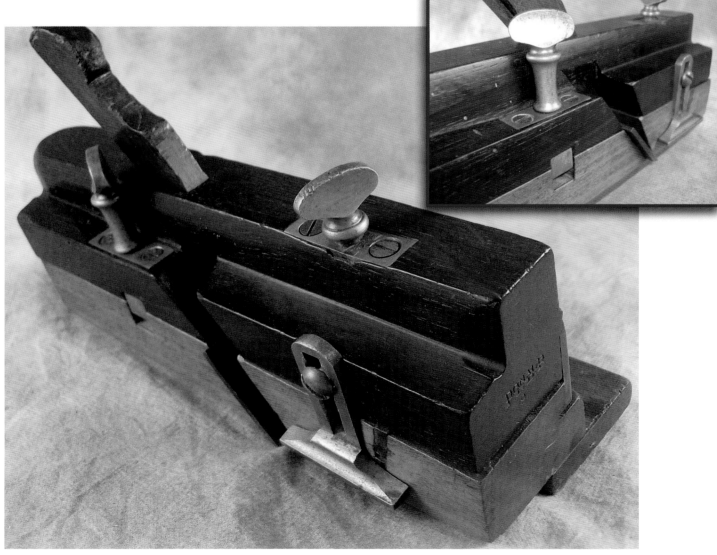

Inventor: Thomas D. Worrall

Origin: Charlestown, Massachusetts

Patent Number & Date: 11,635; August 29, 1854.

Un-handled ebony plane body. Detachable sole.
Two brass locking screws for engaging the "T" shaped
slots in each end of the various interchangeable
soles. Worrall's Multiform patent information marked
on toe. Charlestown, Massachusetts address.

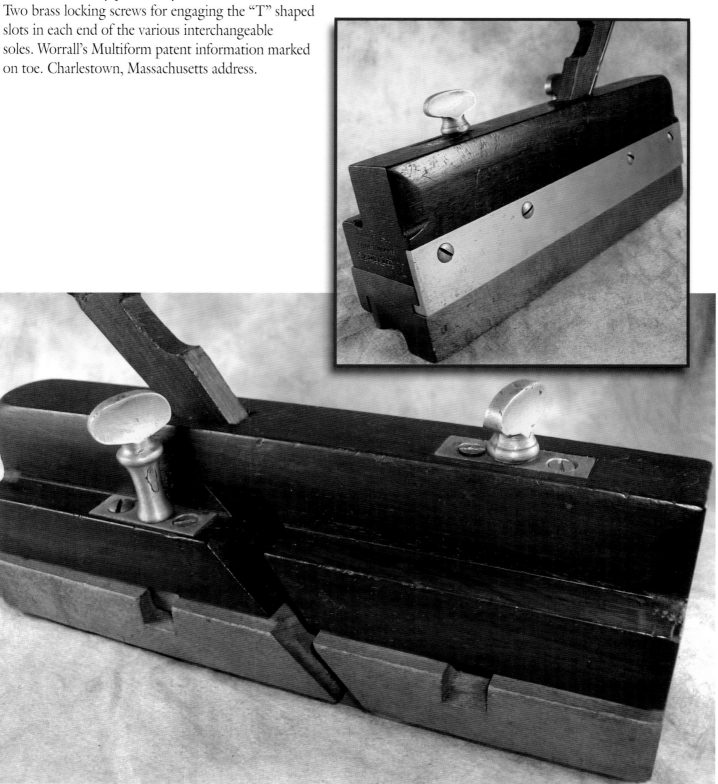

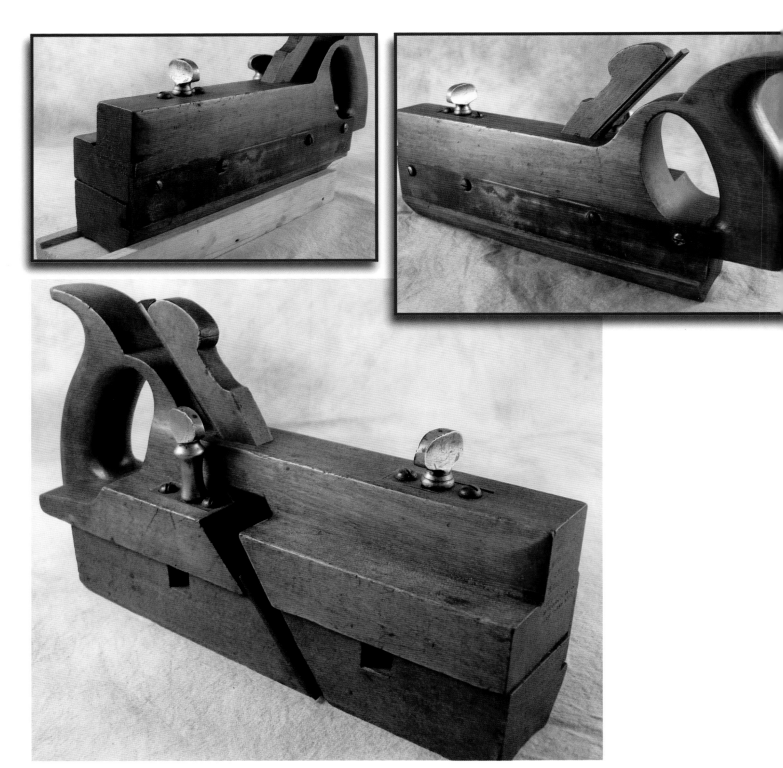

Inventor: Thomas D. Worrall

Origin: Charlestown, Massachusetts

Patent Number & Date: 11,635; August 29, 1854.

(left) Plane with integral handle, beech stock, equipped with two brass locking screws for engaging the "T" shaped slots in each end of the interchangeable soles. Toe of plane stamped with Worrall's patent date. Charlestown, Massachusetts address.

(right and below) Un-handled plane beech stock. Equipped with two brass locking screws for engaging the "T" shaped slots in each end of the interchangeable soles. Patent date marked on toe with the Charlestown Massachusetts address.

Multiform
Patent Planes *Continued*

Inventor: Thomas D. Worrall

Origin: Columbus, Ohio

Patent Number & Date: 11,635; August 29, 1854.

Ohio Tool Company licensed by Multiform Moulding Plane Company to manufacture its patented line of planes. Plank match groove plane (below), has a screw arm adjustable fence. Plane marked No. "82".

The tongue plank plane (right), has a screw arm adjustable fence. Plane marked "82".

Multiform
Patent Planes *Continued*

Inventor: Thomas D. Worrall

Origin: Columbus, Ohio

Patent Number & Date: 11,635; August 29, 1854.

Combination match plane "Tongue and Groove".
Two single slots, one on each end, to accommodate
a single slot handle. One handle used on either
end for cut selected. One end marked "5/8", other
end marked with Worrall patent information and
"OHIO TOOL CO."

Inventor: Thomas D. Worrall

Origin: Mount Holly, New Jersey

Patent Number & Date:
11,635; August 29, 1854.

Un-handled Multiform beech plane body.
Detachable sole. One slot only locked
by a screw rear of blade wedge. Depth stop
and adjustable fence. Toe stamped with
Worrall's 1854 patent.

Multiform Patent Planes *Continued*

Inventor: Thomas D. Worrall

Origin: Mount Holly, New Jersey

Patent Number & Date: 11,635; August 29, 1854.

(top photo) Four single slot Multiform bead molding planes. Owner's mark "A. M. DAVIS" on toe and heel. All planes have recessed heel feature and appear to be factory made.

(bottom photo) Single slot comparator to double slotted Multiform sole.

Inventor: Multiform Moulding Plane Company

Origin: Mount Holly, New Jersey

Patent Number & Date:
11,635; August 29, 1854.

A set of eighteen hollows and rounds.
Single slotted soles.

Inventor: Thomas D. Worrall

Origin: Mount Holly, New Jersey

Patent Number & Date:
18,312; September 29, 1857.

A selection of Multiform Moulding
Plane Company's detachable
handles. Top three handles covered
by Thomas D. Worrall's
Patent No. 18,312.

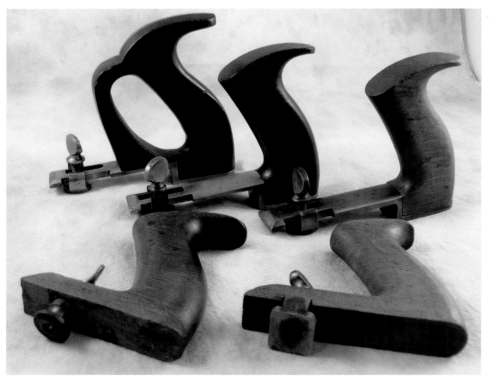

Multiform
Patent Planes *Continued*

Inventor: Thomas D. Worrall

Origin: Mount Holly, New Jersey

Patent Number & Date: 11,635; August 29, 1854.

Plow plane all boxwood except for detachable handle which is rosewood. Single "T" slot for detachable handle was originally for a double slotted interchangeable base. Red arrow shows front slot filled in for use with revised single slot version. Toe marked "MULTIFORM MOULDING PLANE COMPANY PATENTED AUG. 29 1854". Thomas Worrall patent.

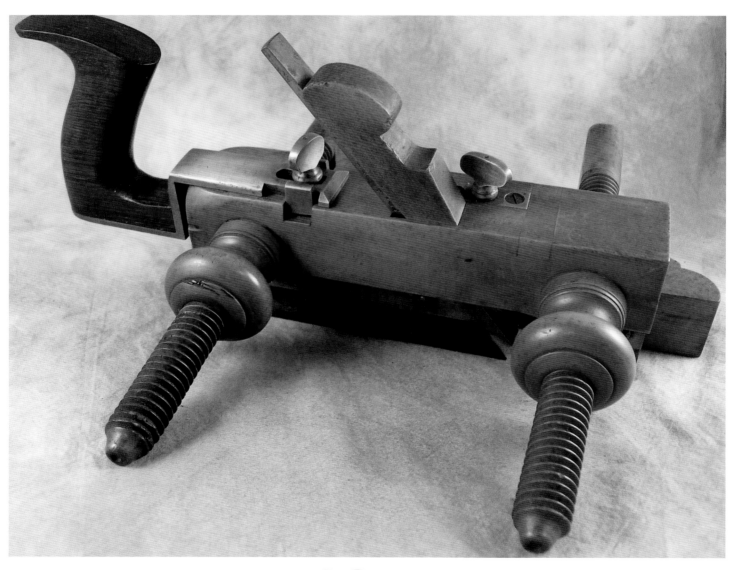

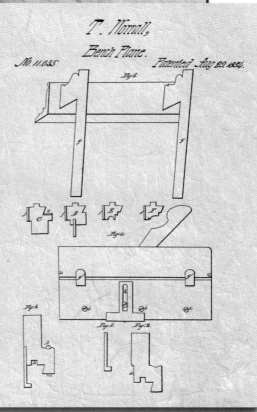

Multiform Patent Planes *Continued*

Inventor: Multiform Moulding Plane Company

Origin: Charlestown, Massachsetts

Patent Number & Date: None.

A conventional style boxwood block plane. Double iron marked "HUMPHREYVILLE MANUFACTURING CO." Toe stamped "MULTIFORM MOULDING PLANE CO. CHARLESTOWN, MASS." Multiform evidently supplied conventional style planes to customers that did not require handles. This block plane is an example of this.

Wood
Plow Planes

Owasco Plow Plane

Inventor: Owasco Tool Company

Origin: Auburn, New York

Patent Number & Date: Circa 1875-1893.

Screw-arm boxwood plow plane with ivory tips. Toe marked "OWASCO TOOL CO NEW YORK" and No. "96". Owasco was a trade name of Auburn Tool Company and later Ohio Tool Company after its merger with Auburn Tool Company in 1893.

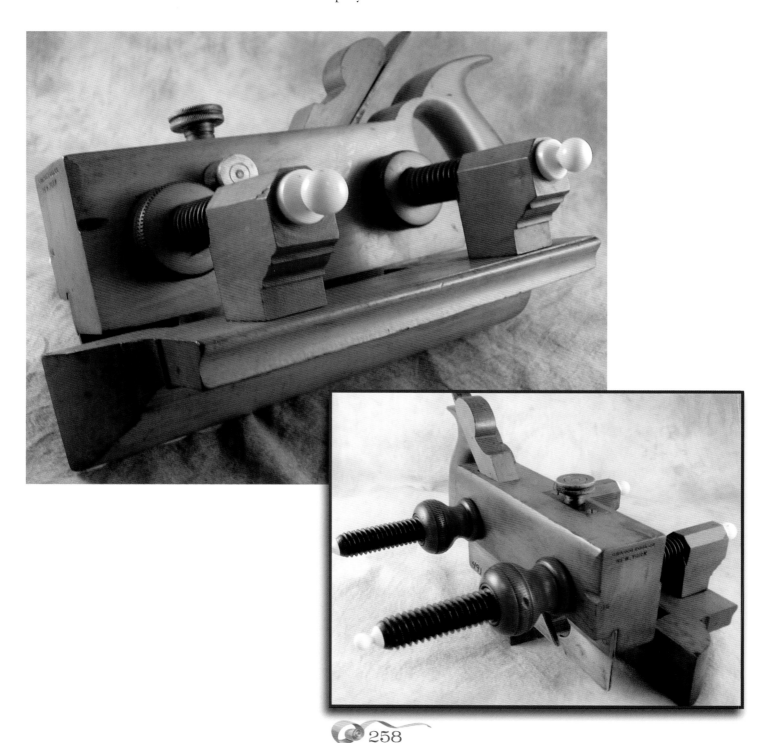

Appleton Plow Plane

Inventor: Thos. L. Appleton

Origin: Boston, Massachusetts

Patent Number & Date: Circa 1875 - 1879.

Screw-arm ebony and boxwood plow plane. Boxwood arms, knobs and wedge. Toe marked "THOs L. APPLETON BOSTON".

Lamb Plow Plane

Inventor: J. H. Lamb

Origin: New Bedford, Massachusetts

Patent Number & Date: Circa 1869 - 1874.

Screw-arm rosewood and boxwood plow plane. Boxwood wedge, arms and knobs. Boxwood fence with rosewood insert. Toe stamped "J.H. LAMB NEW BEDFORD".

Cumings Plow Plane

Inventor: A. Cumings

Origin: Boston, Massachusetts

Patent Number & Date: Circa 1848 - 1854.

Screw-arm ebony and boxwood plow plane. Boxwood fence, arms and knobs. Ebony wedge. Toe marked "A. CUMINGS BOSTON".

Ohio Tool Co. Ivory-tipped Plow Plane

Inventor: Ohio Tool Company

Origin: Columbus, Ohio

Patent Number & Date: None; Circa 1860.

Ebony plane with 6 ivory tips. Rosewood bridle with boxwood spindle.
An 1860 Ohio Tool Company catalog advertised the No.113 as
the "Self adjusting improved plane that won first premium award
at the 1853 New York World's Fair."

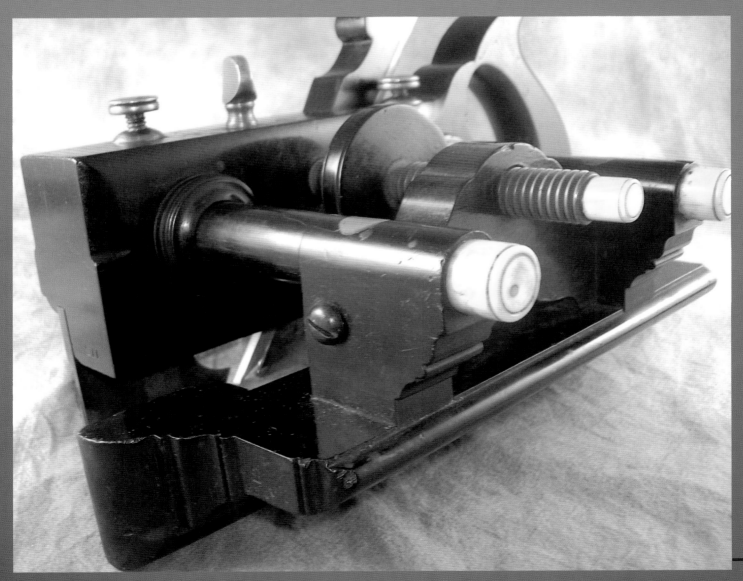

Arrowmammett Plow Plane

Inventor: Arrowmammett Works

Origin: Middletown, Connecticut

Patent Number & Date: Circa 1850.

Screw-arm beech plow plane with boxwood arms, knobs and wedge. Toe stamped "ARROWMAMMETT WORKS MIDDLETOWN". Arrowmammett was the trade name for the Baldwin Tool Company, Middletown, Connecticut.

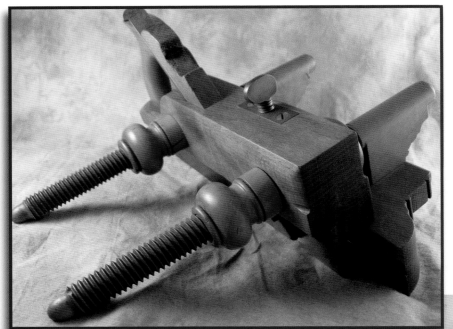

Pearce Plow Plane

Inventor: J. W. Pearce

Origin: Fall River, Massachusetts

Patent Number & Date: Circa 1853.

Plow plane, sliding wood arms, thumb screw arm locks. Beech body, ebony wedge. Toe marked "J.W. PEARCE" stamped three times in a triangular shape with 1853 in the middle and six floral devices. Metal "skate" fence.

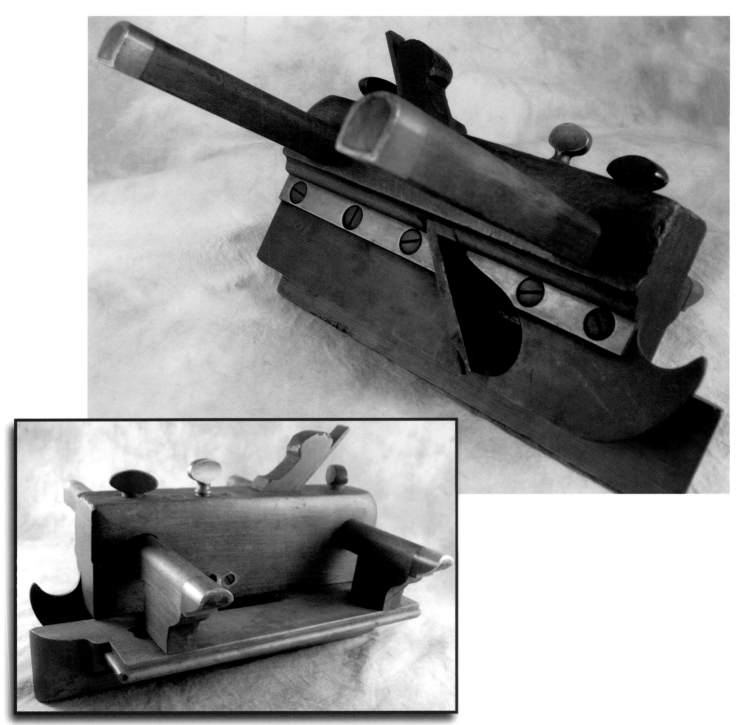

Andrus
Plow Plane

Inventor: Andrus

Origin: Newark, New Jersey

Patent Number & Date: Circa 1821-1841.

Three arm plow plane. Bridle design with a steel screw that adjusts body sides along friction fit arms. Fence position is locked by means of a brass thumb screw. Front arm incorporates an inlaid wear plate.

Sandusky Plow Plane

Inventor: Sandusky Tool Company

Origin: Sandusky, Ohio

Patent Number & Date: Circa 1869 - 1925.

Sandusky Tool Company ebony plow plane with four ivory tips. Toe stamped "SANDUSKY COMPANY" in "banner" logo and No. 137.

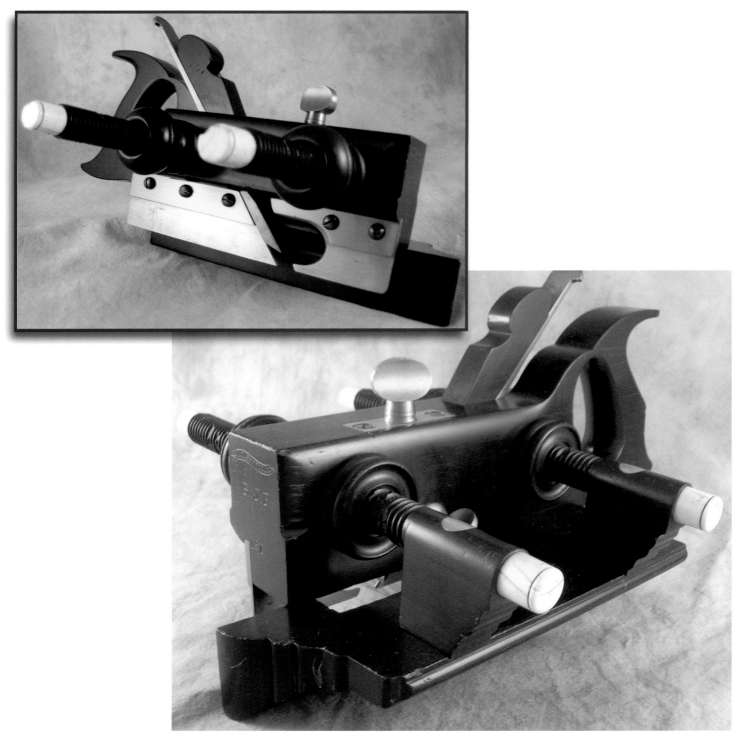

Sanborn Plow Plane

Inventor: D. P. Sanborn

Origin: Littleton, New Hampshire

Patent Number & Date: Circa 1840-1871.

Un-handled beech slide arm plow plane.
Wood thumb screws lock arms. Wood depth stop.
Toe marked "D.P. SANBORN LITTLETON, N.H."

Denison
Plow Plane

Inventor: G.W. Denison & Company

Origin: Winthrop, Connecticut

Patent Number & Date: Circa 1868 - 1884.

Screw-arm plow plane with rosewood body, wedge and threaded arms. Boxwood knobs and locking nuts. Toe marked "G.W. DENISON & CO WINTHROP CONN."

DeForest Plow Plane

Inventor: DeForest

Origin: Birmingham (Derby), Connecticut

Patent Number & Date: Circa 1860.

Un-handled boxwood screw-arm plow plane.
Toe marked "DEFOREST BIRMINGHAM".

Beattie Plow Plane

Inventor: Israel O. Beattie

Origin: Middletown, New York

Patent Number & Date: Circa 1854-1870.

Un-handled boxwood screw arm plow plane. Boxwood arms, lock-nuts and wedge. Toe marked "ISRAEL O. BEATTIE MIDDLETOWN".

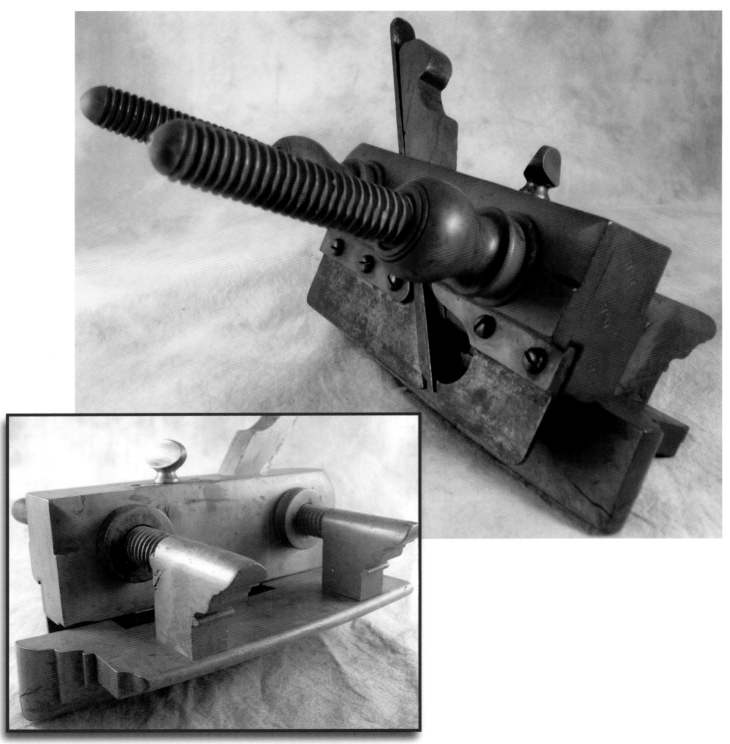

Brown Plow Plane

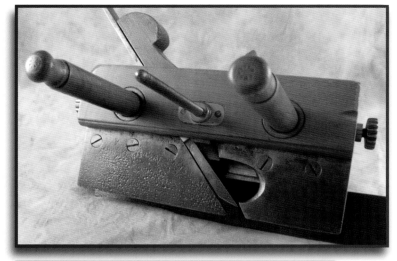

Inventor: Brown Tool Company

Origin: Unknown

Patent Number & Date: Possibly circa 1880.

Three arm bridle beech plow plane. A steel threaded rod adjusts the fence. Body locked in place with 2 thumb screws; one on each end of the plane. "BROWN TOOL CO." Stamped on iron. This plane is believed to be a modification of one of James Brown's patents.

Camper Plow Plane

Inventor: Napolean Camper

Origin: Baltimore, Maryland

Patent Number & Date: Circa 1850.

Two arm bridle plow plane. Rosewood with ivory decorative strip between the arms. Ivory double dovetailed wear strips are incorporated in the fence. Plane was a presentation piece for Samuel Spurrier, a Baltimore carpenter. Brass plate on bridal inscribed "Samuel Spurrier"

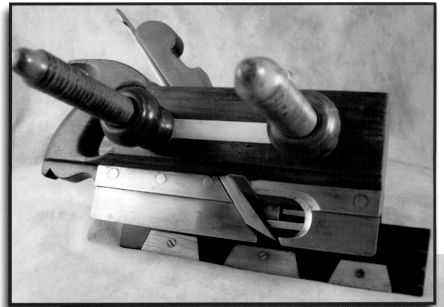

Ward
Plow Plane

Inventor: William Ward

Origin: New York, New York

Patent Number & Date: None Known.

Three arm plow plane with a threaded steel center rod which passes through a brass insert in the body. Wood arms are connected to the center rod above the fence and at the end of the wood arms. The center rod is locked in place with the use of two brass thumb screws.

Ebony Plow Plane

Inventor: Unknown Maker

Origin: Unknown

Patent Number & Date: None Known.

Screw-arm plow plane. Ebony body and wedge. Arms are brass and threaded. Ebony knobs and brasslocking washers. Most likely made by a craftsman for his own use.

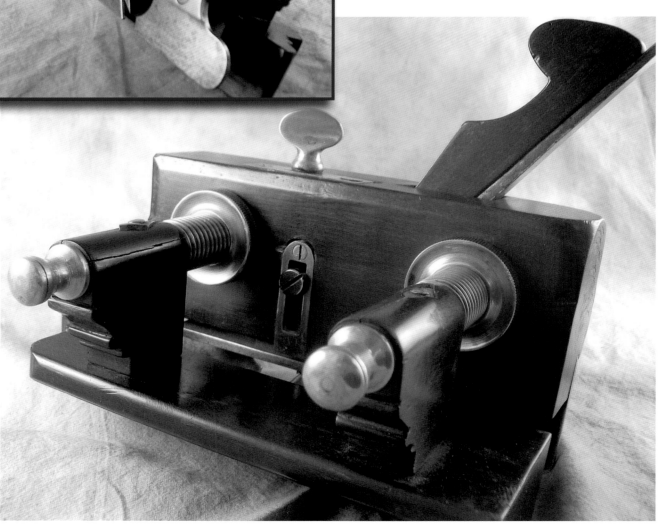

Lewis
Plow Plane

Inventor: J. H.. Lewis

Origin: New York, New York

Patent Number & Date: None Known.

Three arm plow plane. Center wooden adjusting screw moves fence in and out to select the desired width. Iron stop with finger grip top.

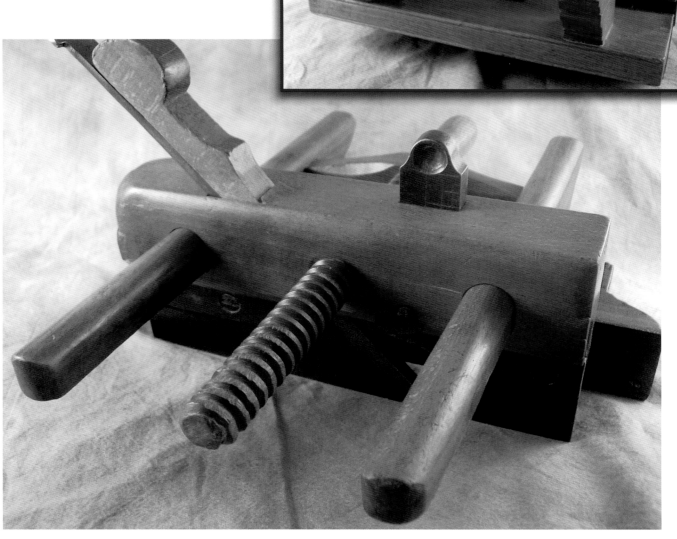

Shelton & Osborn Plow Plane

Inventor: Shelton & Osborn Mfg. Co.

Origin: Birmingham, Connecticut

Patent Number & Date: Circa 1850.

Handled screw-arm plow, ebony and boxwood. Ebony body, boxwood arms, knobs, nuts and washers. Toe marked "SHELTON & OSBORN MFG. CO. BIRMINGHAM CT."

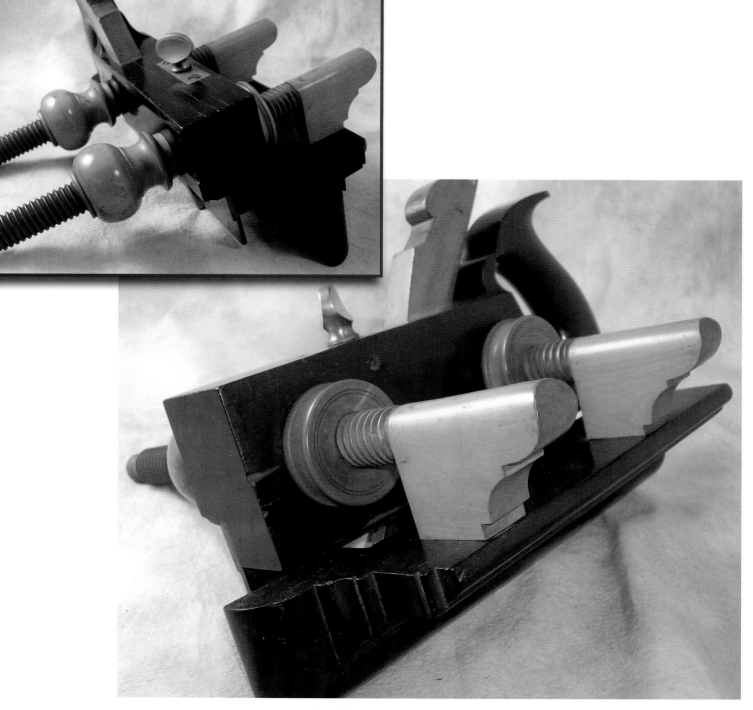

Ohio Tool
Plow Plane

Inventor: Ohio Tool Company

Origin: Columbus Ohio

Patent Number & Date: Circa 1851-1913.

Screw-arm applewood plow plane with integral handle. Boxwood arms and knobs. Toe stamped "T. DAVIES" in banner logo and "101 1/2".

Wood Patent
Plow Planes

Chapin-Rust Patent Plow Planes

Inventor: E. M. Chapin - Solon Rust

Origin: Pinemeadow, Connecticut

Patent Number & Date: 76,051; March 31, 1868.

E. M. Chapin - Solon Rust patented self adjusting three-arm plow plane. 10 1/2" lg x 6" w. Beech body brass arms 5 1/2" lg. Center wood screw. "PATENT MAR. 31, 1868" stamped on right side.

Chapin-Rust
Patent Plow Planes *Continued*

Inventor: E. M. Chapin - Solon Rust

Origin: Pinemeadow, Connecticut

Patent Number & Date:
76,051; March 31, 1868.

Chapin-Rust patented self adjusting plow plane. Beech body. Steel arms with center adjusting screw that regulates the fence. Patent date stamped on right side. Toe stamped "UNION FACTORY - WARRANTED - NO. 238 1/2".

Solon R. Rust *1833-1908*

Chapin-Rust
Patent Plow Planes *Continued*

Inventor: E. M. Chapin - Solon Rust

Origin: Pinemeadow, Connecticut

Patent Number & Date:
76,051; March 31, 1868.

E. M. Chapin - Solon Rust patented self-adjusting three arm plow plane. Beech body. Steel arms attached to body with a bridle on center arm. Toe marked "NO. 239 3/4."

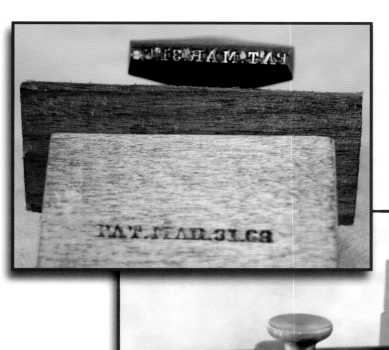

Patent date stamp for E. M. Chapin - Solon Rust plow planes. Actual factory stamp "MARCH 31, 1868." Mark usually found on right side of self adjusting plow planes.

Carpenter
Patent Plow Planes

Inventor: E.W. Carpenter

Origin: Lancaster, Pennsylvania

Patent Number & Date: 594; February 6, 1838.

Plow plane. Beech body, rosewood nuts and boxwood arms. Rosewood handle with brass support plate. Nose stamped "CARPENTER IMPROVED ARMS AND HANDLE LANCASTER".

Carpenter
Patent Plow Planes *Continued*

Inventor: Emanuel W. Carpenter

Origin: Lancaster, Pennsylvania

Patent Number & Date:
594; February 6, 1838.

Patented plow plane; "CARPENTER'S PATENT IMPROVED ARMS LANCASTER" stamped on toe. Boxwood body with boxwood arms. Rosewood nuts, washers and fence support. Turned knobs at end of arms for adjusting the fence. Double lock nuts feature secures fence in place.

White
Patent Plow Plane

Inventor: Israel White

Origin: Philadelphia, Pennsylvania

Patent Number & Date: 7951X; October 23, 1839.

Three arm patented plow plane, 9 3/4" lg x 8 3/4" w, including arms. Ebony wedge and arms. Beech body. Fence faced in ebony. Bridle type adjustment. A single knob adjustment for fence. Brass depth stop and fittings. Plane marked 160.

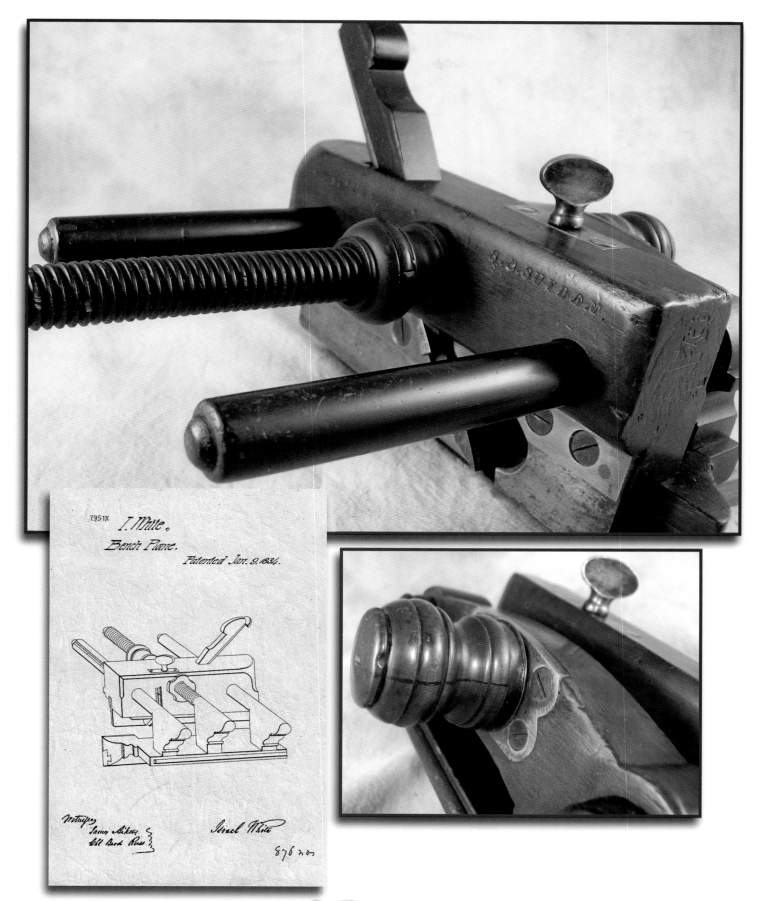

Sandusky Patent Plow Plane

Inventor: Harmon VanBuskirk

Origin: Vienna, Michigan

Patent Number & Date:
97,328; November 30, 1869.

Patented plow plane made by Sandusky
Tool Company. Brass center wheel self regulating
plow. Rosewood body with boxwood arms.
"SANDUSKY TOOL CO. NO. 40"
stamped on toe.

Multiform
Patent Plow Plane

Inventor: Multiform Moulding Plane Company

Origin: Mt. Holly, New Jersey

Patent Number & Date: 11,635; August 29, 1854.

Patented un-handled plow plane. Ebony body and wedge. Boxwood arms and knobs. Two brass locking screws engage "T" shaped slots in interchangeable sole. Toe marked "MULTIFORM MOULDING PLANE CO. PAT'D AUG 29, 1854" Thomas Worrall patent.

Laskey Patent Block Plane

Inventor: Stephen G. Laskey

Origin: Chelsea, Massachusetts

Patent Number & Date: 306,763; October 21, 1884.

Patented cast brass block plane. Dovetailed steel/sole/cutting iron. The adjustable sole (also the cutting iron) is adjustable and locked in position by use of two brass locking nuts located behind the frog. Front nose piece is adjustable.

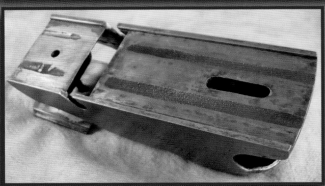

Spotlight Plane

Metal Patent
Plow Planes

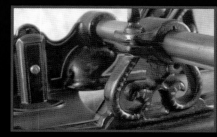

Miller Patent Plow Planes

Inventor: Charles G. Miller

Origin: New Britain, Connecticut

Patent Number & Date: 131,367; September 17, 1872.

Gunmetal light plow plane believed to be Stanley's earliest attempt at a combination plane. This design was quickly superseded by the traditional Miller patent plow plane. Gunmetal handle integral with the frame. Rosewood knob attached to front arm.

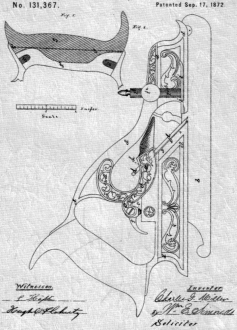

C. G. MILLER.
Improvement in Carpenters' Plows.
No. 131,367. Patented Sep. 17, 1872.

3 Sheets--Sheet

Miller Patent
Plow Planes *Continued*

Inventor: Charles G. Miller

Origin: Brattleboro, Vermont

Patent Number & Date: 104,753; June 28, 1870.

Stanley's first model No. 41 Miller's patent combination plane. Iron frame. Japanned with rosewood handle and brass screws. "hook and hump" frame profile. 10 1/2" lg x 5 1/2" w.

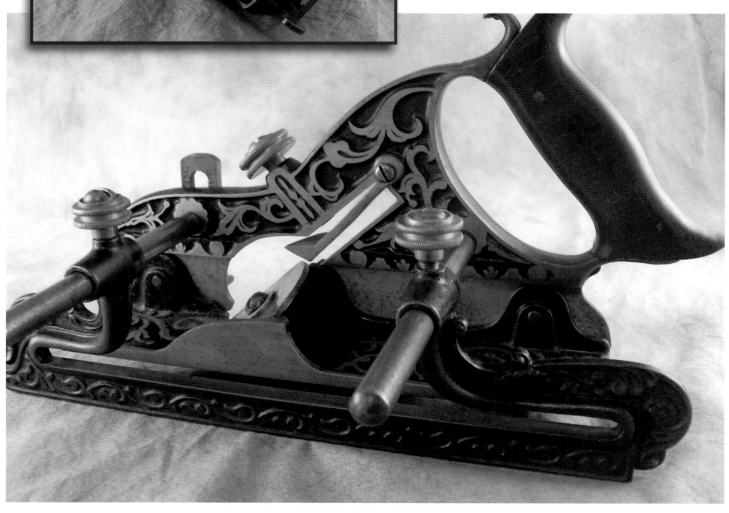

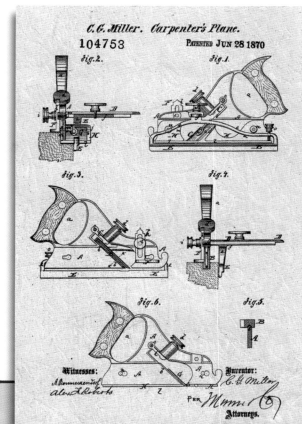

Miller Patent Plow Planes *Continued*

Inventor: Charles G. Miller

Origin: Brattleboro, Vermont

Patent Number & Date: 104,753; June 28, 1870.

Stanley's first model Miller's patent combination plane No. 42 (below). Gunmetal with japanning filling in the recesses. Rosewood tote, brass locking screws. Type 1 with "hook and hump" frame profile. Oval trademark 10 1/2" lg x 5 1/2" w. Manufactured by the Stanley Rule & Level Co.

Stanley's No. 43 Miller's patent combination plane (right). Type 1 with wrap around fence. Rosewoond handle and brass screws. "hook and hump" frame profile.

Miller Patent Plow Planes *Continued*

Inventor: Charles G. Miller

Origin: Brattleboro, Vermont

Patent Number & Date: 104,753; June 28, 1870.

Miller's patent combination plane. Iron fence and frame (below). 10 1/4" lg x 6 1/2" w, including arms. Brass screws. Skate stamped "STANLEY RULE & LEVEL CO. NO. 43."

Miller's patent combination plane (right). Gunmetal frame and fence. 10 3/4" lg x 6" w, including arms. Rosewood handle, iron filletster bottom. Manufactured by Stanely Rule & Level Co. No. 42, second model type 2.

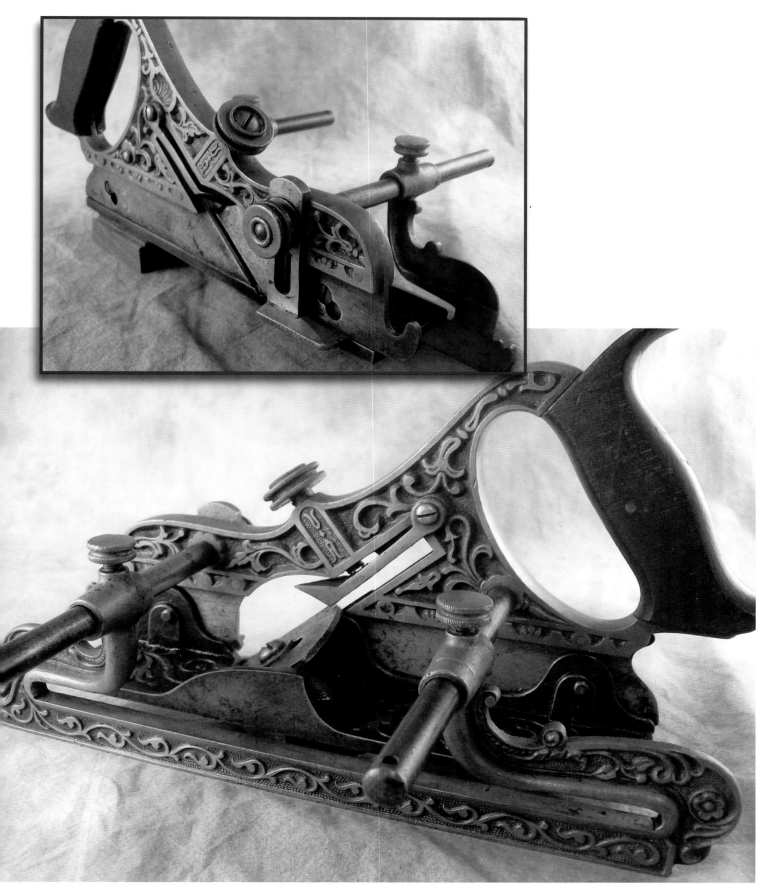

Miller Patent Plow Planes *Continued*

Inventor: Charles G. Miller

Origin: Brattleboro, Vermont

Patent Number & Date: 104,753; June 28, 1870.

Miller's patent combination plane (below). Iron fence and frame. 9" lg x 6" w, including arms. Brass screws. Fence has "4" hole feature. "STANLEY" cast in center of fence. Plane equipped with slitter and depth gauge.

Miller's patent combination plane (right), 10 3/4" lg x 6" w. including arms. Brass screws. Manufactured by Stanely Rule & Level Co. Extra fence was standard equipment and filletster bottom was iron even on the gunmetal planes.

Walker Patent Plow Plane

Inventor: Edwin Walker

Origin: Erie, Pennsylvania

Patent Number & Date: 318,331; May 19, 1885.

Plow plane, iron frame, 10 1/2" lg. Rosewood handle. Equipped with 15 double ended cutters providing 30 shapes. Adjustable face plate. Face formed in any shape by adjusting plates to desired bit.

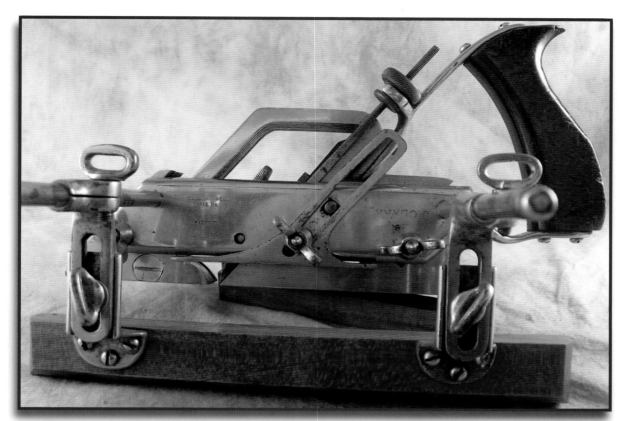

Edwin Walker *1847-1917*

No. 1 Size
Iron Smooth Planes

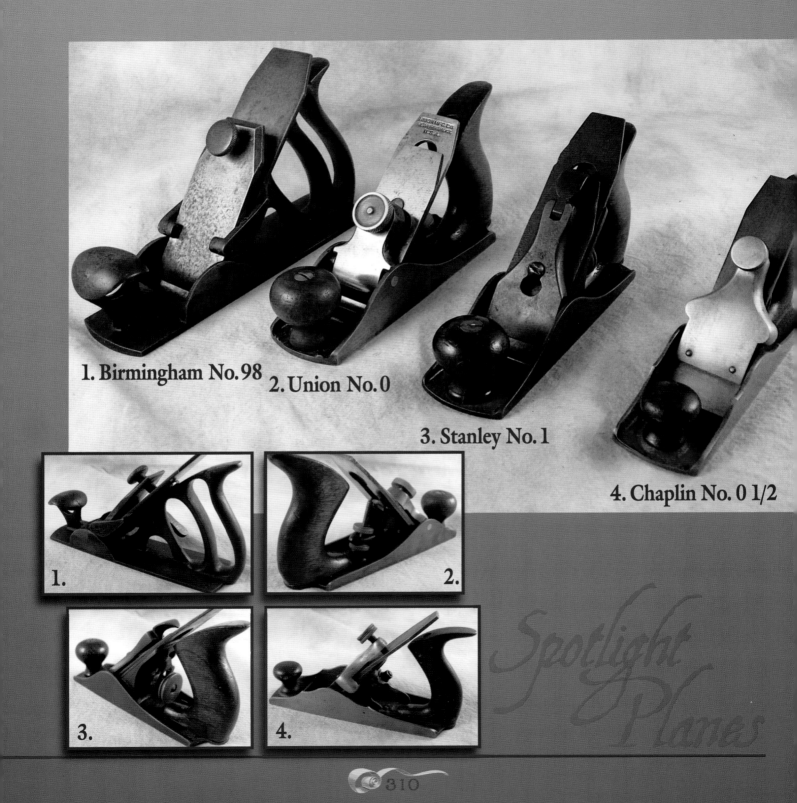

1. Birmingham No. 98

2. Union No. 0

3. Stanley No. 1

4. Chaplin No. 0 1/2

1.

2.

3.

4.

Spotlight Planes

Morris Patent Plow Plane

Inventor: Ellis H. Morris

Origin: Canton, Ohio

Patent Number & Date: 112,949; March 21, 1871.

Morris' iron plow plane 9" lg x 4" w closed. "Scissor type" adjustable fence. Rosewood handle. Plane came equipped with double-ended cutting irons.

Mayo Patent Plow Plane

Inventor: Matthias Mayo

Origin: Boston, Massachusetts

Patent Number & Date: 167,772; September 14, 1875.

Iron plow plane 11" lg x 7 1/2" w, including arms. Double iron 2" w. Rosewood handle & fence insert. "MAYO" engraved one letter in each of four brass adjustment screws. "THE BOSS PLANE" cast in frame. Bronze paint. Skate marked "M.C. MAYO PATENT."

Iron non-adjustable Mayo block plane. 7 3/4" lg x 2" w. No known patent. Single iron. Long brass holding screw with letter "M" in script identical to that used in Mayo's plow planes brass locking screws. Bronze paint.

Loughborough Patent Plow Plane

Inventor: William S. Loughborough

Origin: Victor, New York

Patent Number & Date: 42,485; May 3, 1864.

Iron plow plane 11" x 2" excluding fence. Brass screws for locking fence and cutter. Beech wood handle. "G & J TELFORD, MAN FRS. ROCHESTER, N.Y." cast into side of frame. Manufactured by G. & J. Telfords 1866 through 1868 only.

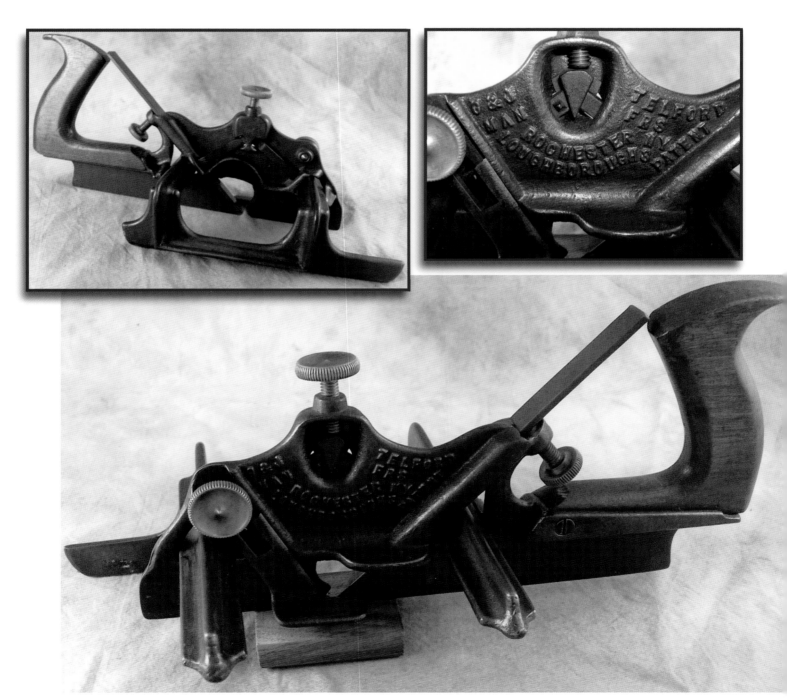

Fales Patent Plow Planes

Inventor: Amos Fales

Origin: Denver, Colorado

Patent Numbers & Dates:
254,542; March 7, 1882
295,916; August 1, 1884
348,198; August 31, 1886

Iron combination plow plane 10 1/4" lg x 6 1/2" w, including arms. Rosewood handle and knob. It takes two detachable plates for each cutter.

Twelve woodworking profile sets (36 pieces) for Fales Patent
Iron Combination Plane. Each profile requires one iron plus
two plates. Fales advertised his plane could do over 80 profiles,
thus requiring 160 plates.

Phillips Patent Plow Planes

Inventor: Russell Phillips

Origin: Gardiner, Maine

Patent Number & Date: 67,671; August 13, 1867.

Iron frame plough plane (below), 9 3/4" lg x 7 1/2" w, including arm. Overall length including fence and frame 11". Rosewood handle and partial fence trim. Brass screws. T-handle bolt arm lock. No marks on skate. Patent assigned to Russell Phillips and Nathan Weston.

Iron plough plane (right), 10 1/2" lg x 8" w, including arms. Oval stamp on skate. Stamped on both sides "PHILLIPS PLOUGH PLANE PAT'D AUG 13, 1867. MANF'D BY BOSTON TOOL CO. 22 KILBY ST. BOSTON." Fence and body stamped "#30."

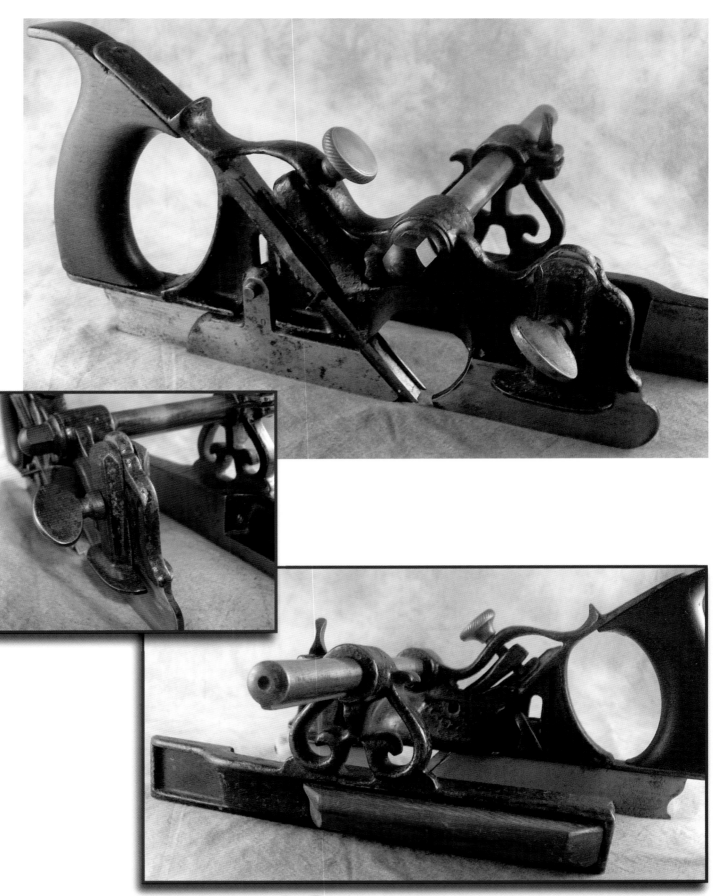

Phillips Patent
Plow Planes *Continued*

Inventor: Russell Phillips

Origin: Boston, Massachusetts

Patent Number & Date:
Phillips' improved model circa 1872.

Russell Phillips' improved plough plane.
Iron frame, 10 1/2" lg x 8" w, including arms.
Overall length including frame and fence 12".
"M.C. MAYOS IMPROVED PLANE" painted
on fence. Oval stamp with "BABSON &
REPPLIER - 7 DOANE ST" on skate.
Rosewood handle and partial fence piece.
Black japanning with gold and red pinstripe trim.

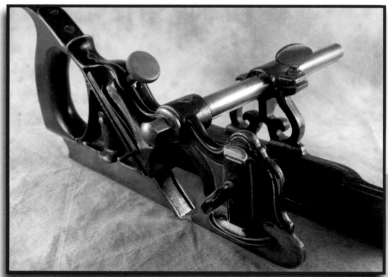

Metallic Plane Co.
Plow Plane

Inventor: Metallic Plane Company

Origin: Auburn, New York

Patent Number & Date: No Known Patents.

Iron plow plane. Rosewood handle. Steel screws to secure arms. "METALLIC PLANE CO– AUBURN, NY" stamped on skate.

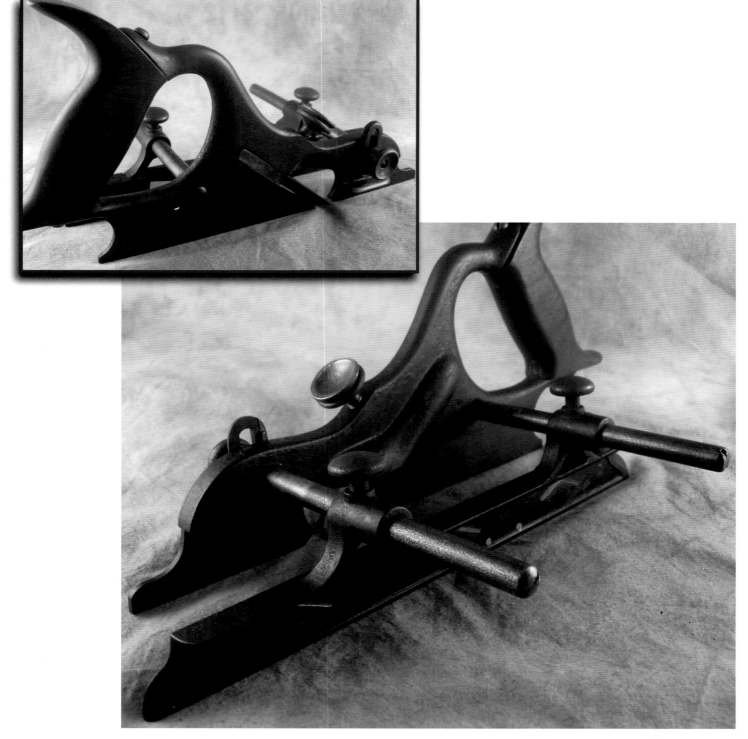

Siegley Patent Plow Planes

Inventor: Jacob Siegley

Origin: New York, New York

Patent Number & Date: 216,979; July 1, 1879.

Actual wooden patent model for Siegley combination plane submitted to U.S. Patent Office. Patent office tag and ribbon shown with plane model. Wood model matches patent drawing to the "letter" right down to two wooden cutters. Model made of pine.

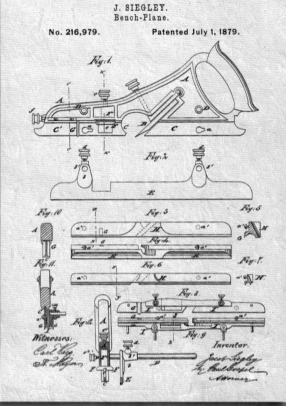

Spotlight Plane

Siegley Patent Plow Planes *Continued*

Inventor: Jacob Siegley

Origin: Wilkes-Barre, Pennsylvania

Patent Number & Date: 294,919; March 11, 1894.

Iron combination plane (below), 10" lg x 8" w. Rosewood handle and fence Nickel plated and japanned frame. Cutter held by thumbscrew on left side of frame.

Iron combination plane (right), 9 1/2" lg x 8" w, including arms. Beech handle and fence. Brass washers with steel screw inserts to secure fence to arms. Lever adjustment.

Siegley Patent Plow Planes *Continued*

Inventor: Jacob Siegley

Origin: New York, New York

Patent Number & Date: 216,979; July 1, 1879.

Iron combination plane, 10 5/8" lg x 7 1/2" w, including arms. Maple handle. Steel locking screws. No marks, but design is identical to Siegley's first patent.

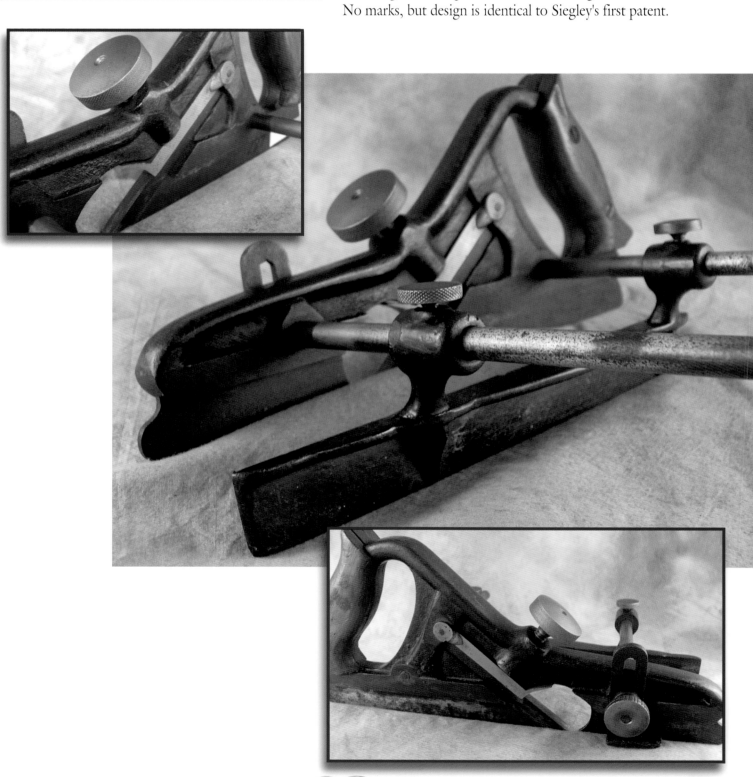

18th Century
Wood Planes

18th Century Wrentham, Massachusetts Planes

Below, left to right:

Sam Druce; Ce. Chelor; I. Nicholson;
F. Nicholson; G. Hawes.

Sam Druce

Ce. Chelor

I. Nicholson

F. Nicholson

G. Hawes

18th Century Massachusetts Planes

Below, left to right:

H. Wetherel; Jn Tower; L. Little; S. Dean;
I. Iones; S+Pomeroy; S Doggett.

H. Wetherel - Norton

I. Iones - Holliston

S+Pomeroy - N'hampton

Jn Tower - Rutland

S Doggett - Dedham

L. Little - Boston

S. Dean - Dedham

18th Century
Massachusetts Planes *Continued*

Below, left to right:

W. Raymond; I. Sleeper; EZ, Baxter;
E. Clark; A. Smith.

W. Raymond - Beverly

I. Sleeper - Newburyport

EZ, Baxter - Yarmouth

E. Clark - Middleboro

A. Smith - Rehoboth (dated 1815)

18th Century
Connecticut Planes

Below, left to right:

S. Branch; R. Fosdick; W. Harris; A. Hide;
Joseph Clark; W. Sprat; A. Woodward.

S. Branch - Lisbon

Joseph Clark - Middletown

R. Fosdick - New London

W. Sprat - Farmington

W. Harris - New London

A. Woodward - New London

A. Hide - Norwich

18th Century Connecticut Planes *Continued*

Below, left to right:
B-French; O:Spicer; H.Wetherell; I. Fitch; J. Harris.

B-French - Chapinville

O:Spicer - North Groton

H. Wetherell - Chatham

I. Fitch - Lebanon

J. Harris - Waterbury

Miscelleneous
18th Century Planes

Below, left to right:

N. Briggs; Jo, Fuller; I. Lindenberger; S. King;
Ion. Ballou; Isaac Field; Tho. Grant.

N. Briggs - Keene, N.H.

Ion. Ballou - Providence, R. I.

Jo, Fuller - Providence, R. I.

Isaac Field - Providence, R. I.

I. Lindenberger - Providence, R. I.

Tho. Grant - New York

S. King - New England

18th Century Plow Planes

I. Lindenberger - Providence, R. I.

I. Sleeper -
Newburyport, Mass.

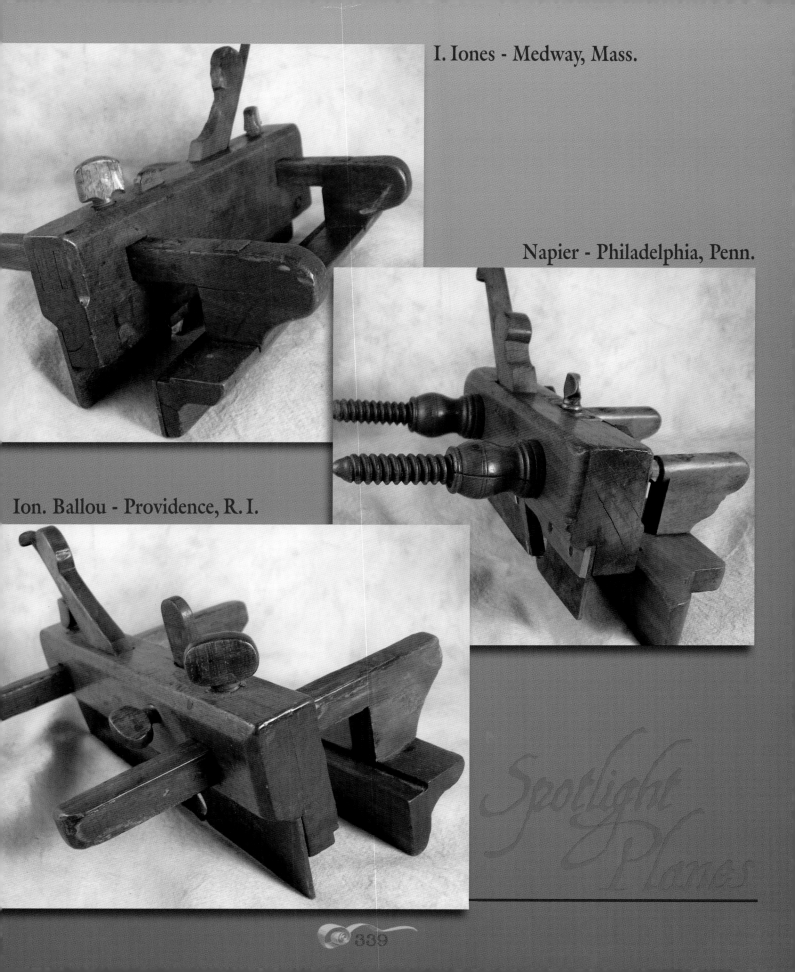

I. Iones - Medway, Mass.

Napier - Philadelphia, Penn.

Ion. Ballou - Providence, R. I.

Index

Index *Continued*